Acknowledgments

I am excited to announce my second scientific research book titled **Bending Strength of Circular-Arc-Tooth-Trace Cylindrical Gear: Theoretical Modelling and Experimental Validation** is published. It took me ten months to finish this book. Many people offered their assistance in constructing and writing this book. They deserve a word to be grateful.

First of all, I wish to express my deepest gratitude to my three supervisors, Professor Xueyong Zhao, Associate Professor Lijun Wang, and Associate Professor Yihong Shi, for the valuable instruction. You guided and advised me throughout my research when I was a master's degree candidate from 1987 to 1990. I appropriate you had been my supervisors and colleagues.

Second of all, I wish to state my sincere thanks to my big family, ten members. I would like to tell you that you almost did your best support for me to work on this book. Without your spiritual encouragement, it would not have been possible for me to commit my research results to a book.

Third of all, I would like to offer my special gratitude to my parents, two knowledge and educational persons. You contributed your wisdom to mentor me and guard me. No matter what happened, you always told me to be optimistic facing it. Without your enthusiasm, I might not be able to write this book for seeking self-value.

Fourth of all, I would like to salute my husband, a scientist, for several years' dedicated support. I appreciate your patience. You contributed your energy and time to take care of me. I would be lucky to have you as a husband. You devoted your wisdom and provided me extraordinary help to reorganize and translate my master's degree thesis into three international conference articles from 1992-1994. After 24 years, the topics of these articles motivate me to widely search related materials and guide me to figure out much more content and then to fill in my book one chapter by another one.

Thanks to all contributors who related to this book! Your suggestions and the excellent advice provided me with ideas to dig every chapter with greater depth and finally bring the book to completion.

TABLE OF CONTENTS

ABSTRACT i

ACKNOWLEDGEMENTS iii

1. Introduction 1
   1.1 Background Investigation 1
   1.2 Objectives and Significance 4
   1.3 Book Overview 6
2. Forces at CATT Gear Tooth 10
   2.1 Model Simplifications and Basic Assumptions 10
   2.2 Force Equations and Analysis 13
3. Determination of the Critical Section 20
4. Moment of Inertia for Critical Section 25
   4.1 Centroid of the Critical Section 26
   4.2 Moment of Inertia for the Critical Section 29
5. Stress Estimations on the Critical Section 33
   5.1 Estimation of Component Stress on the Critical Section 33
   5.2 Estimation of Equivalent Stress on the Critical Section 38
6. One Case Study of Tooth Stresses on the Root Fillet 41
7. Bending Stress Distributions along the Tooth Trace at Tooth Root Fillet 49
8. Bending Strength of CATT Gear 58
   8.1 Determination of Factors 60
   8.2 Determination of Allowable Bending Stress 66
9. Experimental Test of Bending Stress Distributions along the Tooth Trace at Tooth Root Fillet 70

9.1 Experiment Setup 70

9.2 Model Loading and Strain Acquisition 74

9.3. Case Study and Bending Strength Formula Validation 77

10. Error Analysis and Corrections 84

10.1 Theoretical Error Analysis 84

10.2 Experimental Error Analysis 86

Appendix I: Determination of Tooth Width Factor 90

I.1 Definition of Tooth Width Factor 90

I.2 Effect of Tooth Width Factor on Stress 93

AUTHOR'S NOTE 97

About Author 103

1. Introduction

1.1 BACKGROUND INVESTIGATION

In the heavy construction equipment field, the bearing capacity of gear is of continuous interest [1-6]. It can be improved by varying the geometric parameters of the gear tooth, such as the tooth profile, the tooth trace, the dedendum thickness, the type of contact line, meshing characteristics, etc.. A lot of efforts have contributed to study the effects of tooth profile on the bearing capacity of gears [5]. The involute gear and circular arc gear are two typical examples for this purpose. However, the type of tooth trace is also an important factor. The helical gear, the spiral bevel gear, and the herringbone gear are three typical examples for increasing the contact line to improve gear teeth strength.

In twenty century, the circular-arc-tooth-trace (CATT) bevel gear has been designed, developed, and manufactured by Gleason Corp [2]. Furthermore, this kind of tooth trace has been applied to cylindrical gear, and as a result, a new type of gear, CATT cylindrical gear, was coming [1-8]. Figure 1.1 shows a pair of CATT cylindrical gears, which was manufactured by my supervisor, professor Wang, L.J., in our lab in 1985. It can be imagined as a particular type of CATT bevel gear whose shaft-angle is zero [9]. It is named as circular-arc-tooth trace cylindrical gear [10] and also named as circular-arc curvilinear tooth gear [11], as well as C-gear [13].

Figure 1.2 displays an individual tooth cut off from a CATT cylindrical gear. Its gear tooth trace is a spatial circular-arc. Along with the face-width, the tooth face in one face is the concave tooth surface, and the tooth face in another face is the convex tooth surface. The tooth profile on the middle transverse section is involute (as in the spur gear or the helical gear), and any other transverse tooth profiles are approximately involute. The tooth root thickness increases from the middle transverse section to the two end transverse sections.

Figure 1.1 A Pair of CATT Cylindrical Gears

Comparing with a pair of spur gears, helical gears, and herringbone gears, a pair of CATT gears takes some advantages in industrial use.

In spur gears, the contact line is parallel to the axis of rotation. In CATT gears, the contact begins from a point, goes through spatial curve across the tooth face, and ends at a point. Therefore, the CATT gears gradually engage in the teeth and smoothly transfer load from one tooth to another. This gradual engagement makes the gear operation smoother and quieter than with spur gears and results in a lower dynamic factor. Thus, it can transmit heavy loads at high speeds [12].

In helical gears, the contact line is diagonal across the face of the tooth. Hence, both engaged teeth are subjected to axial load. In CATT gear, the gear tooth is symmetric to the middle transverse section, which looks like two helical gears with opposing helix angles stacked together. Two opposing axial loads cancel in the result of no axial force applied to the shafts. This makes its bearing capacity be improved much more than those of helical gears.

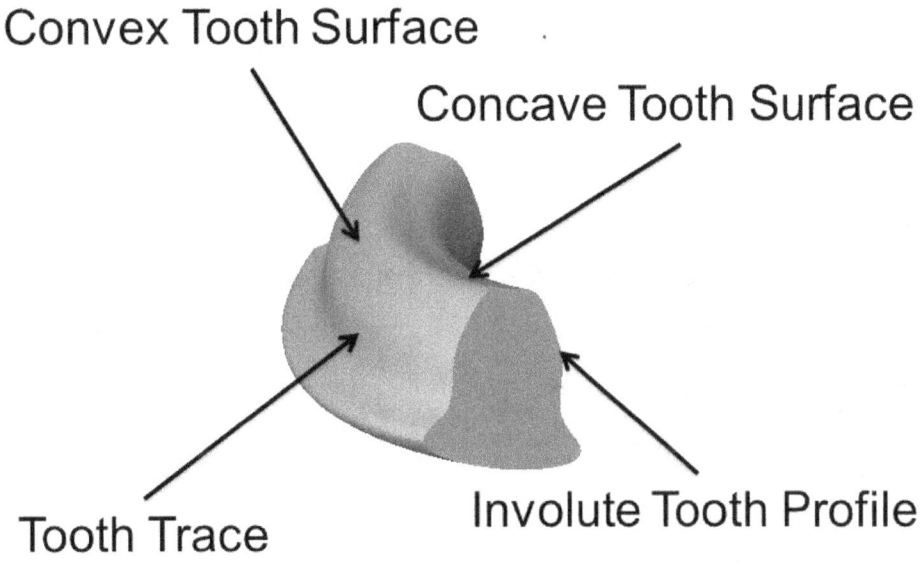

Figure 1.2 Tooth Cut off from CATT Cylindrical Gear

Liking a pair of herringbone gears, the CATT gears heritage its advantage of the elimination of thrust load in gears and overcome its disadvantage of higher machining and mounting costs [12]. This improves their applications in heavy power transmission.

Generally, the CATT gears have excellent meshing performance, driving stationary, high contact ratio, high transmission efficiency, no additional axial force, large load capacity, lower contact, and bending stresses, etc. [10-11]. These advantages eventually promote the CATT gears to be used in heavy vehicles with longer service life and lower vibration frequency, higher stability, and less noise generation than spur gears, helical gears, and herringbone gears. Therefore, the CATT gears' potential applications are being developed by scientists and engineers.

So far, there have been some studies on the CATT tooth bending strength [1-5]. The maximum bending stress analysis at the tooth root fillet is addressed by Luo [3]. He established the maximum bending stress equations at the tooth root fillet by modifying the equations used to the spur cylindrical gear through introducing the arc factor of CATT gear. The result indicates that the critical transverse section should be located in the middle transverse section (the middle of the tooth length).

More detail investigations are conducted by Li and Zhao [4]. In their theoretical calculation, a cantilever model has been proposed to evaluate the bending stress at the tooth root fillet of CATT gear. The result shows that for the concave tooth, the critical transverse sections should be at the two sides; but for the convex tooth, the critical transverse section is at the middle.

Further verifications have been derived by using the strain gauge method to determine the values of bending stresses in CATT gear along the tooth length at the root fillet [5]. The experimental results are in good agreement with Li et al.'s theoretical predictions.

These studies provide a solid foundation for further promoting the CATT cylindrical gear in the engineering applications. In the engineering field, the simplified calculation equations for evaluating tooth bending strength are necessary.

1.2 OBJECTIVES AND SIGNIFICANCE

This book documents my early researches on the bending strength of CATT gear during working on a master degree project. In order to model the bending strength, the bending stress on the tooth must be obtained firstly. Therefore, the predicting and measuring bending stress on the tooth are the priority task in this book. Then, one compensative model of the bending strength is conducted. Constantly, one experimental method of static electric resistance strain gauge is applied to measure the bending stress on the tooth. The objectives of this book are to contribute a theoretical formula and experimental method towards efficient design and analysis of CATT gear.

In engineering applications, the bending strength formula of CATT gear takes a dominant role, even though the modern advanced technology of the finite element analysis method (FEAM) is used to get detailed analysis results. So far, FEAM is more suitable to the graduate student level understanding of stress distributions and may not be accepted by all level engineers.

The bending strength formula of CATT gear is developed base on classic mechanics and heritages the main part of spur gear formula, but modifies and adds some factors. It allows to quickly predict the maximum stress and determine the critical transverse section on the tooth. Eventually, engineers can rapidly estimate tooth strength during the initial design stage. This traditional style of the formula is acceptable by the most engineers who may only hold bachelor degrees or even graduate degrees. Therefore, making the formula more accurate always is paid attention and effort by researchers and engineers.

In the research field, the static electric resistance strain gauge method still is a basic testing method, even though the dynamic measurement method is developed. The static method still has application perspectives widely. This book contains my study of bending strength of CATT gear, which involves not only the theoretical calculation but also the experimental measurement. The proposed static test method builds a fundamental procedure to measure the bending stress distributions along the tooth length at root fillets. It provides means for validation of the theoretical model with the experimental results. This book forms a bridge between the static test method and the dynamic one. And also, it provides a solid foundation for further dynamic modeling and test of bending stresses of CATT gear in the engineering applications.

1.3 BOOK OVERVIEW

This book involves two main topics: the establishment of bending strength formula and development of experimental means for promoting the design and analysis of CATT gear in the engineering application.

Chapter 1 introduces the CATT gear history, development, application, and research. This book's objectives and significance are highlighted. The literature review is narrowed in bending stress studies to fit the topic of the book. An overview of this book is addressed.

Chapter 2 derives the equations of force applied to the tooth of CATT gear based on some simplifications and assumptions. Initially, works focus on simplifying the tooth geometric profile, defining the teeth mesh characteristics, and assuming the tooth loaded forces. Then, works turn to create mathematical models of tooth component forces and their distributed forces in the tangential, radial, normal, and axial directions, respectively.

Chapter 3 establishes mathematical equations of three geometric parameters used to determine the critical section. They are h_F (distance between the critical section and the most unfavorable point), S_F (the width of the critical section) and ρ_F (the fillet radius at the critical section).

Chapter 4 creates the moment of inertia formulas of the critical section about its horizontal neutral axis and vertical neutral axis. Firstly, the centroid of the critical section is computed by dividing the section into three simpler shapes. Secondly, the moment of inertia for each simpler shape is computed about its centroid axis and then calculating the total moment of inertia by parallel axis theorem.

Chapter 5 produces equations of component stresses and equivalent stresses on the critical section. Initially, the bending stress, normal stress, and shear stress are modeled. Then, the equivalent bending stress and the equivalent shear stress are created, individually. Finally, integration of the equivalent bending stress and the equivalent shear stress leads to the general equivalent stress.

Chapter 6 demonstrates a case study of component stresses and equivalent stresses on the critical section at selected points. Stress distributions are plotted and analyzed. And, the maximum stress values and positions are predicted.

Chapter 7 shows a case study of the bending stress distributions along the tooth trace at the root fillet. The efforts of the module, number of teeth, and tooth width factor on the bending stresses are analyzed according to the load applied on the top of the concave tooth and convex tooth, respectively.

Chapter 8 proposes a bending strength formula by modifying the basic bending stress equation by adding more modified factors. The factor determinations and allowable bending stress determinations are addressed in detail.

Chapter 9 develops an experimental procedure to test bending stress distributions along the tooth trace at the root fillet for validating the theoretical model. The strain gauge method is proposed to test the strain at the root fillet. The strain equation is derived from Hooke's law and the bending strength equation. The validation is performed by comparing and analyzing the theoretical results and the experimental results.

Chapter 10 analyzes the theoretical errors and experimental errors. The theoretical errors are addressed by discussing the simplifications and assumptions as creating the bending stress formulas. The experimental errors are analyzed by investigating equipment modification, test device position, and signal measurement.

There is one appendix, which indicates how to determine the tooth width factor of a CATT gear. The tooth width factor is defined by three geometric parameters, such as the tooth width, the reference circular radius, and the central angle. The effect of the tooth width factor on the tooth stress is analyzed, and the range of 0.65-0.75 is suggested.

REFERENCES

1. Fu, D.Q.. 1980. Analysis of the bending strength of CATT cylindrical gear. Journal of Jilin University of Technology, Vol.4, No.21, pp. 11-14.
2. Peng, F.H.. 1978. Research for broaching arc tooth cylindrical gear, Natural Science Journal of Jilin University of Technology, No.1, pp.14-30.
3. Luo, M.. 1987. Bending Strength of CATT Cylindrical Gear. M.S. Thesis, Beijing University of Iron and Steel Technology, China.
4. Li, Y. and Zhao, X.Y.. 1993. Bending Stress Analysis of CATT Cylindrical Gear. Proceedings of the First China/Japan International Symposium on Machine Element, Nov.6-8, Beijing, P. R. China, pp.196-200.
5. Li, Y. and Zhao, X.Y.. 1996. Bending Stress at the Tooth Fillet in the CATT Cylindrical Gear. Proceedings of the Second China/Japan International Symposium on Machine Element, Nov.17-19, Wuxi, P. R. China, pp.215-218.
6. Li, Y. and Zhao, X.Y.. 1997. Distributions of Bending Stress at the Tooth Fillet along the Tooth Length in the CATT Cylindrical Gear. The International Conference on Mechanical Transmissions and Mechanisms, July 1-4, Tianjin, P. R. China, pp.649-652.
7. Erricello, R.. 1978. Bending Stress in Gear Teeth having Circular Arc Profiles-Part I: Analysis. Tran Sanctions of the SAME, Vol. 100, No. 4.
8. Palletdb, A.. 1986. Dynamic Load on the CATT Cylindrical Gear. Mechanical Manufacturing, No. 2.
9. Sonoda, K., Takenouchi, K., and Hashimuras.. 2014. Design and Manufacture of New Circular-Arc Tooth-Trace Gears. The 3rd International Conference on Design Engineering and Science, ICDES.

10. Zhang, Q.L., Hou, R. and Tang, G.W.. 2016. Method of Processing and an Analysis of Meshing and Contact of Circular Arc Tooth Trace Cylindrical Gears. Transactions Of Famena XI-4 , pp.11-14.
11. Wu, Y.C., Chen, K.Y., Tsay, C.B. and Ariga, Y.. 2009. Contact Characteristics of Circular-Arc Curvilinear Tooth Gear Drives. Journal of Mechanical Design, Vol. 131, No.8, pp.1-8.
12. Bhandai, V.B., 2013. Introduction to Machine Design, Second Edition. McGraw Hill Education, New Delhi.
13. Arafa, Hu., 2005. C-Gears: Geometry and Machining. ARCHIVE Proceedings of the Institution of Mechanical Engineers Part C Journal of Mechanical Engineering Science, 219(7), pp.709-726.

2. Forces at CATT Gear Tooth

In this Chapter, the forces applied to the tooth of CATT gear are derived based on some simplifications and assumptions. Initially, works focus on simplifying the tooth geometric profile, defining the tooth mesh characteristics, and assuming the tooth loaded forces. Then, works turn to create mathematical models of tooth component forces and their distributed forces in the tangential, radial, normal, and axial directions, respectively.

2.1 MODEL SIMPLIFICATIONS AND BASIC ASSUMPTIONS

In the procedure evaluating the bending stresses on the tooth root fillet of a CATT gear, the first step is to establish the mathematical equations of meshing forces applied on the tooth. Before starting this work, it is necessary to make some simplifications and basic assumptions.

- The contact line of a pair of CATT gear teeth is assumed as a planar circular arc along with the tooth trace.

Actually, while a pair of CATT gears engages in contact, the initial contact is a point and then the contact changes into a line. As the teeth come into more engagement, the contact extends all the way across the tooth face with a series of complex spatial curves. The final contact becomes a point again.

For the purpose of a convenient building mathematical model, each contact line is simplified to a planar circular arc, which can be a segment of a reference circle of the tooth trace. And its circumference length equals the arc length of the reference circular.

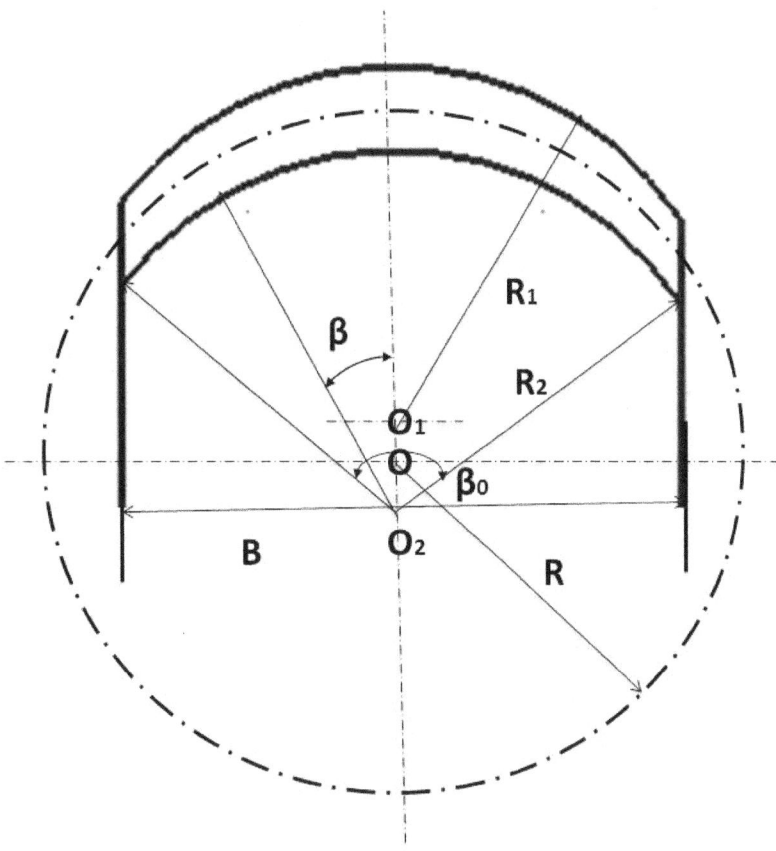

Figure 2.1 Tooth trace of a CATT Cylindrical Gear with Defined Geometric Parameters

Figure 2.1 visualizes the simplified CATT tooth trace with the geometric parameters of the tooth width B, central angle β_0, helix angle β, as well as radii of the reference circular R_1 and R_2 on the convex and concave surfaces, respectively. Where, $R_1=R+(1+C)m*\tan 20°$ and $R_2=R-(1+C)m*\tan 20°$. C is the radial clearance factor and equal to 0.25. And also, m is the module of the CATT gear (Shanghai Metallurgical Machinery Company, 1984). In this research, they are defined to be equal to the curvature radius of tooth trace, R, at pitch cycle, $R_1=R_2=R$.

- For calculating the tooth root fillet stress, it's assumed that the load is applied on the top of a single tooth, and the friction on the tooth surface is neglected.

The number of pairs of CATT gear teeth in contact simultaneously varies from one to two or more as the teeth rotate through the loading zone. To maximally capture the forces loaded on the tooth, it is customary, however, to assume that the contact ratio is one. That means only a pair of teeth is in the mesh.

Figure 2.2 shows an individual tooth of CATT gear with the general normal force P_n applied over the contract arc on the cylindrical surface of the addendum.

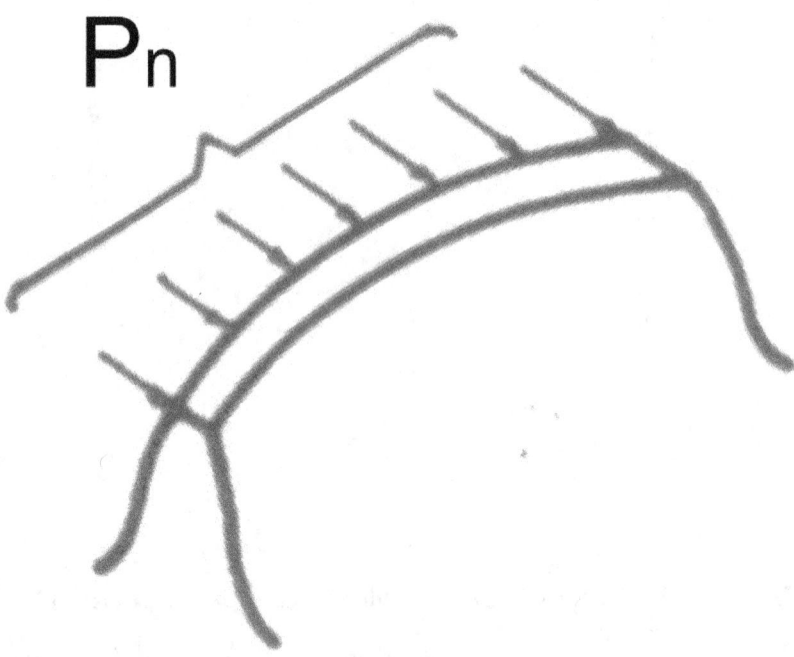

Figure 2.2 A separated CATT Gear Tooth with Normal Force at Addendum

- The tooth profile of a CATT gear is assumed to have a standard involute at any transverse section through the face width. The method establishing the tooth force equations of a spur gear is employed to the CATT gear.

In fact, as introduced in Figure 1.2, the transverse profile of a CATT gear tooth presents a standard involute only on the middle transverse section, and approximately involutes on any other transverse profile. Therefore, the meshing characteristics of the gear are similar to those of spur gear at any arbitrary transverse section.

2.2 FORCE EQUATIONS AND ANALYSIS

Figure 2.3a illustrates the total tooth force P_n acted on the tooth top of a CATT gear, which can be resolved into two components of tangential force P_t and radial force P_r. P_t does transmit the power and P_r does not work but tends to push the gears apart. Vectors of three components can be related by pressure angle at addendum circle α_n in a plane. There is no axial component force because of the elimination of opposing axial loads in symmetrical tooth face.

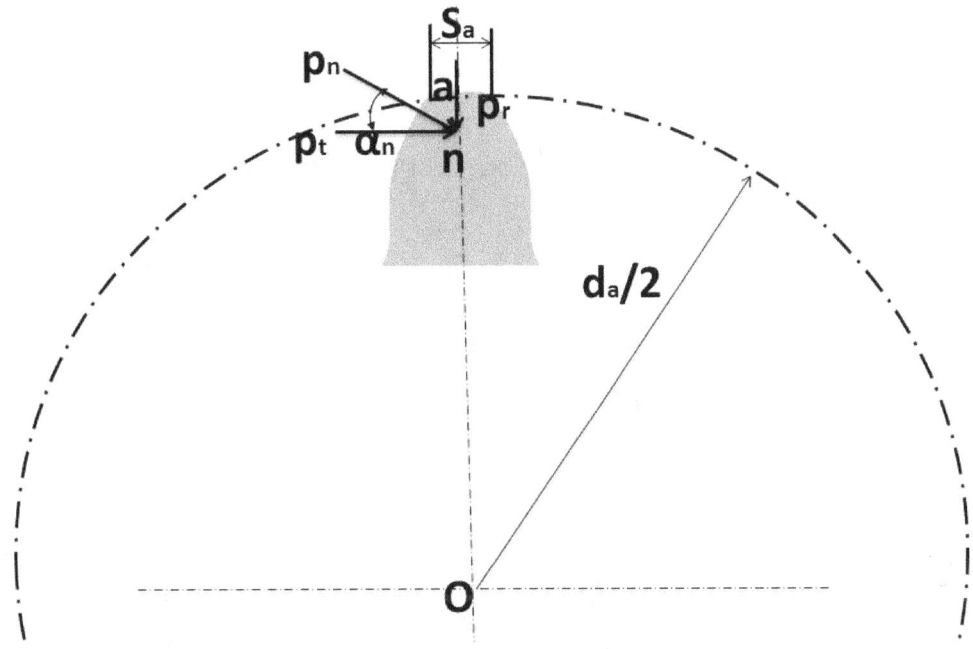

Figure 2.3a Total Tooth Forces Acted on Tooth Top of CATT Gear

Figure 2.3b indicates that the vectors of distributed component forces applied at a selected contact point. The distributed normal force p_n acted on the tooth is divided into distributed tangential force p_t, distributed radial force p_r, and distributed axial force p_a. Comparing to three component forces, the distributed component forces involve four items, which add one more distributed axial force. The vectors of four components are related by pressure angle α_n and helix angle β in three-dimensional space.

These component forces and their distributed forces are modeled as the mathematical equations in the tangential, radial, normal, and axial directions, respectively.

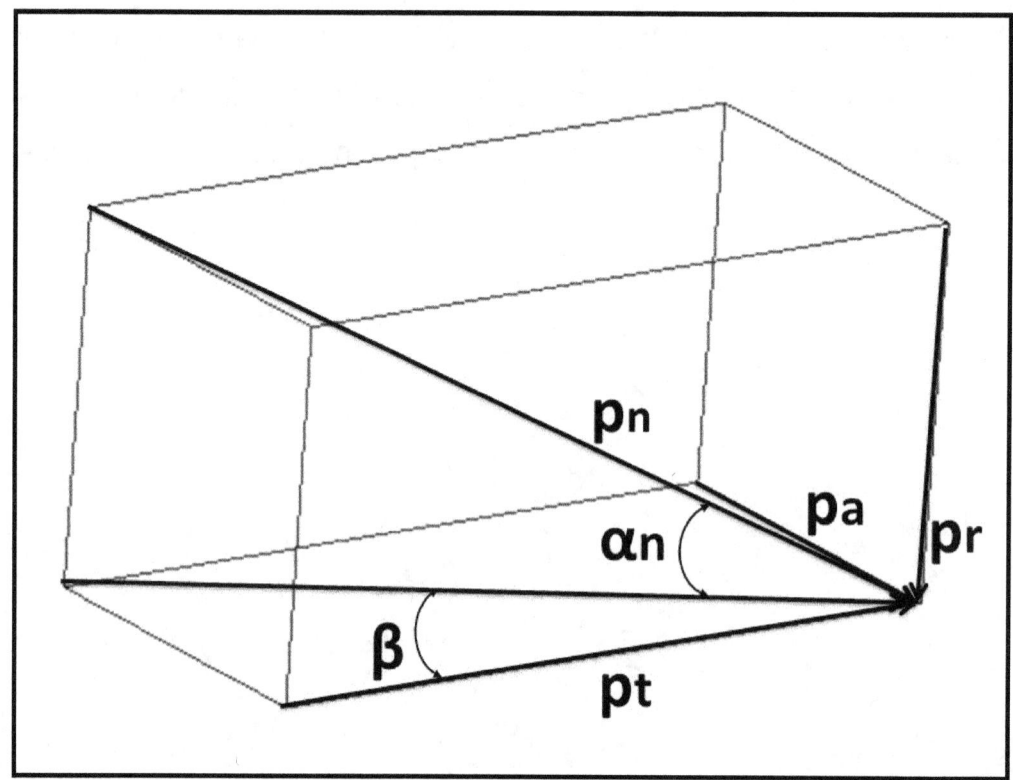

Figure 2.3b Distributed Component Forces Acted on the CATT Tooth Surface at Addendum Circle

1. Tangential Force

The force component associated with power transmission is only the tangential component force P_t. As shown in Figure 2.3a, assuming it is applied on the tooth top point n, which is the intersection of normal component force and central line of addendum circle at the middle transverse section. Resolved P_t can be written as Equation 2.1.

$$P_t = \frac{T}{oa - na} = \frac{2T}{d_a - S_a \tan \alpha_n} \qquad (2.1)$$

where T is the torque generated on the gear, d_a is the diameter of addendum circle, S_a is the tooth thickness at addendum circle, and α_n is the pressure angle at addendum circle.

Assuming the distribution of tangential component force along the circular arc is uniform or same. It is known that the curvature radius of the contact arc equals to R. The distributed tangential force p_t is given as Equation 2.2.

$$p_t = \frac{P_t}{\beta_o R} = \frac{2T}{(d_a - S_a \tan \alpha_n)\beta_o R} \qquad (2.2)$$

In Equation 2.2, for a given gear, the geometric parameters at the addendum circle, such as the diameter d_a, tooth thickness S_a, pressure angle α_n, reference circular radius R and central angle β_o, keep constants, respectively. Once the torque acted on the gear is given, the distributed tangential force will stay unchanged. That validates the assumption of the distribution of tangential component force along the circular arc is uniform.

2. Radial Force

In Figure 2.3b, referring to the geometric relationship of the distributed tangential force p_t, pressure angle α_n, and helix angle β, the distributed radial force p_r can be calculated by Equation 2.3.

$$p_r = \frac{p_t \tan \alpha_n}{\cos \beta} = \frac{P_t \tan \alpha_n}{\beta_o R \cos \beta} \qquad (2.3)$$

When the distributed tangential force p_t and pressure angle α_n are defined, the distributed radial force p_r can be determined by the helix angle β. It increases with the increase of helix angle β from the middle transverse section to the two ends. The minimum value occurs at the middle transverse section, and the maximum one does at the two ends.

Equation 2.3 shows that the distributed radial force p_r is centrally symmetric. Integrating it from the negative half central angle $\beta_o/2$ to the positive one $\beta_o/2$, the total radial component is written as Equation 2.4a.

$$P_r = \int_{-\frac{\beta_o}{2}}^{\frac{\beta_o}{2}} p_r R d\beta = p_t R \tan \alpha_n \ln \frac{1+\varphi}{1-\varphi} \qquad (2.4a)$$

where tooth width factor $\varphi = \sin(\beta_o/2)$ (see Appendix I).

Substituting Equation 2.2 into Equation 2.4a, Equation 2.4b is yielded.

$$P_r = \frac{1}{\beta_o} P_t \tan \alpha_n \ln \frac{1+\varphi}{1-\varphi} \qquad (2.4b)$$

Equation 2.4b builds the relationship between the total radial tooth force acted on CATT gear and the total radial tooth force on the spur gear. For spur gear, it is only $P_r = P_t \tan \alpha_n$. For CATT gear, constant $\frac{1}{\beta_o} \ln \frac{1+\varphi}{1-\varphi}$ is added.

3. Normal Force

In Figure 2.3b, viewing the three-dimensional geometric relation of the distributed tangential force p_t, pressure angle α_n, and helix angle β, the distributed normal force p_n can be established as Equation 2.5.

$$p_n = \frac{p_t}{\cos \alpha_n \cos \beta} \qquad (2.5)$$

Similarly, when the distributed tangential force p_t and pressure angle α_n are set, the distributed normal force p_n is generated as a function of the helix angle β. It increases with the increase of helix angel from the middle transverse section to the two ends. The minimum value appears at the middle transverse section, and the maximum one does at the two ends.

Equation 2.5 illustrates that the distributed normal force p_n has a symmetric plane through the middle transverse section. Integrating it from the negative half central angle $\beta_o/2$ to the positive one $\beta_o/2$, the total normal component is expressed as Equation 2.6a.

$$P_n = \int_{-\frac{\beta_o}{2}}^{\frac{\beta_o}{2}} p_n R d\beta = \frac{p_t R}{\cos \alpha_n} \ln \frac{1+\varphi}{1-\varphi} \qquad (2.6a)$$

Substituting Equation 2.2 into Equation 2.6a, Equation 2.6b is produced.

$$P_n = \frac{1}{\beta_o} \frac{P_t}{\cos \alpha_n} \ln \frac{1+\varphi}{1-\varphi} \qquad (2.6b)$$

In Equation 2.6b, it notes the relationship between the total normal tooth force acted on spur gear and CATT gear. For spur gear, it is only $P_n = \frac{P_t}{\cos \alpha_n}$. For CATT gear, constant $\frac{1}{\beta_o} \ln \frac{1+\varphi}{1-\varphi}$ is added.

Furthermore, comparing Equations 2.4b to 2.6b, the relationship between total normal tooth force and radial force can be expressed as Equation 2.6c.

$$P_n = \frac{P_r}{\sin \alpha_n} \qquad (2.6c)$$

In this point, it can be seen that there are same expression for both spur and CATT gears.

4. Axial Force

In Figure 2.3b, checking the plane geometric relationship of the distributed tangential force p_t and helix angle β, the distributed axial force p_a can be represented by Equation 2.7.

$$p_a = p_t \tan \beta \qquad (2.7)$$

When the distributed tangential force p_t is obtained, the distributed axial force p_a is calculated as a function of the helix angle β. It increases with the increase of helix angel from the middle transverse section to the two ends. The minimum value locates in the middle transverse section, and the maximum one does at the two ends.

Equation 2.7 illustrates that the distributed axial force p_a presents central symmetry. Integrating it between the negative half central angle $\beta_o/2$ and the positive one $\beta_o/2$, the total axial component is written as Equation 2.8.

$$P_a = \int_{-\frac{\beta_o}{2}}^{\frac{\beta_o}{2}} p_a \, R d\beta = 0 \qquad (2.8)$$

The integral result shows that the total axial force equals to zero. That verifies the CATT gear is free from axial thrust due to self-centered characteristics of its teeth.

Reviewing Equations 2.3, 2.5 and 2.7, three distributed forces p_r, p_n and p_a are all derived as a function of the helix angle β. They can be changed at the different meshing points along with the contact arc due to the different helix angle β. They increase with the increase of helix angel from the middle transverse section to the two ends. The minimum values happen at the middle transverse section, and the maximum ones do at the two ends.

Reviewing Equations 2.1, 2.4b, 2.6b and 2.8, total tooth force P_n, as well as its components of tangential force P_t, and radial force P_r have the same or different calculating equations from the spur gear. In Equation 2.1, P_t depends on the power torque T, which heritages the traditional equation of spur gear. In Equations 2.4b and 2.6b for respectively calculating P_r and P_n have added a constant related to central angle β_o. Equation 2.8 indicates that there is no axial component force p_a because of the elimination of opposing axial loads in symmetrical tooth trace through over the middle transverse section.

REFERENCES

1. Shanghai Metallurgical Machinery Company.1984. Strength Design and Analysis of a Circular Arc Tooth Trace Cylindrical Gear. Project Annual Report, No.1, Pp. 1-20.

3. Determination of the Critical Section

The critical section, also called the weakest section, is one of the vital parameters to evaluate the bending stress of CATT gear tooth. There are three geometric parameters used to determine the critical section, which are h_F (distance between the critical section and the most unfavorable point), S_F (the width of the critical section) and ρ_F (the fillet radius at the critical section). Their mathematical equations are established in this Chapter.

The theoretical and experimental studies show that the method of Hofer $\theta=30°$ tangential line can be applied to determine the position of the critical section of CATT gear (Fu, 1980; Li, 1990; Fan, 1979). θ is the tangential angle and is defined as the angle between the centerline of a tooth profile and the tangential line to root fillet curve.

Theoretically, Li (Li, 1990) proposed an image function method to find a critical section of the CATT gear tooth. It is different from spur gear that a CATT gear tooth profile presents a standard involute on the middle transverse section, and any other transverse tooth profiles are approximately involute. The tooth root thickness increases from the middle transverse section to the two end transverse sections.

The geometric parameters of the CATT gear are specified as: number of teeth is Z=19, module is m=5 mm, pressure angle (or profile angle of the cutting tool) is $\alpha=20°$, reference radius is R=69.5mm, tooth width factor is $\varphi=0.72$, central angle is $\beta_o=92°$, and tangential force is $P_t=1000N$.

Two loading cases are selected to calculate the weakest section positions, respectively. For case one, the tangential force is applied on the top of the tooth. For case two, the tangential force is acted on the pitch circle.

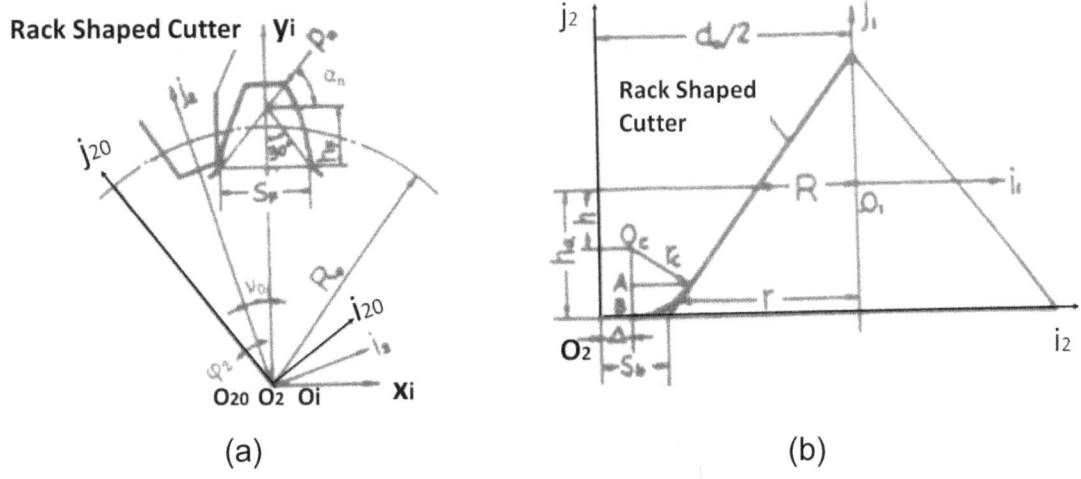

Figure 3.1 A Schematic Diagram of a Tooth Profile and a rack Shaped Cutter at a Selected Transverse Section. The Symbols Used in Equations 3.1-3.3 are Labeled

The calculated results of the two cases show that the highest stress appears in the root section, where $\theta=30°$. Therefore, for an individual tooth, the critical section determined by the Hofer $\theta=30°$ method does not change with the variety of the loading position. Experimentally, stresses developed by normal force in a photo-elastic model of spur involute gear tooth show the highest stress occurs at the fillet region near the base of the tooth (Fan, 1979).

In Chapter 2, the tooth profile of a CATT gear is assumed to have a standard involute at any transverse section through the face width. Thus, this experimental result from the spur gear is suitable for the CATT gear.

Figure 3.1 shows a schematic diagram of a tooth profile and a rack shaped cutter at a selected transverse section. The symbols used in Equations 3.1-3.3 are labeled.

Figure 3.1a indicates the schematic diagram of a tooth fillet formation of CATT gear by cutting with a rack shaped cutter. Three Cartesian coordinates are attached, which are:

- A local Cartesian coordinate o_i (x_i, y_i) is attached to the CATT gear at the center o_i and axis y is fixed to the centerline of a tooth profile.
- An original Cartesian coordinate o_{20} (i_{20}, j_{20}) is attached to the CATT gear at the center o_{20}.
- A local Cartesian coordinate o_2 (i_2, j_2) is attached to the rack shaped cutter at the center o_2 and axis j_2 is fixed on the centerline of the profile.

The geometric parameters labeled in Figure 3.1a are indicated below.
- γ_o is defined as the angle between axis j_2 and axis y.
- φ_2 is defined as the angle between the axis j_2 and j_{20} axes.
- R_0 is the pitch circle radius of the CATT gear.
- α_n is the pressure angle at the addendum circle of CATT gear tooth.
- S_F is the width of the weakest section of CATT gear tooth.
- h_F is the distance between the weakest section and the most unfavorable point of CATT gear tooth.

Figure 3.1b illustrates a transverse section of a rack shaped cutter used to machine the CATT gear, as well as a reference circular cone, which side edge length equals to the length of the sharp edge of the rack shaped cutter. Two Cartesian coordinates are involved in this figure, which are:
- A local Cartesian coordinate o_1 (i_1, j_1) is established in this circular cone at center o_1 and axis j_1 coincides with the centerline of the circular cone.
- The local Cartesian coordinate o_2 (i_2, j_2) has been described in Figure 3.1a.

The geometric parameters labeled in Figure 3.1b are explained below.

- R is the pitch radius of the reference circular cone, which equals to the reference circular radii on the convex and concave surfaces of the CATT gear tooth.
- r is the root radius of the reference circular cone.
- d_o is the distance between axis j_1 and j_2 axes.
- o_c is the curvature center of the rack shaped cutter fillet.
- $h=h_a-r_c$, h_a is the addendum height of the rack shaped cutter, and r_c is the fillet radius of the rack shaped cutter.
- Δ is the half flat top width of the rack shaped cutter measured from the j_2 axis.
- S_b is the half top edge width of the rack shaped cutter measured from the j_2 axis.

In Figure 3.1a, the distance h_F between the weakest section and the most unfavorable point can be expressed as Equation 3.1.

$$h_F = R_o \left[\frac{\cos \alpha}{\cos \alpha_n} - \sin\left(\delta + \frac{\pi}{6}\right) \right] + \sin\frac{\pi}{6}\left(\frac{h}{\cos \delta} + r_c \cos \beta \right) \tag{3.1}$$

where α is the profile angle of the rack shaped cutter, and δ is the rotation angle of the CATT gear. The geometric parameter δ means the gear is rotated around center o_i by an angle δ with respect to the original coordinate o_{20} (i_{20}, j_{20}), and it is given by Equation 3.1a.

$$\delta = \frac{\pi}{2} - \left(\varphi_2 + \gamma_o + \frac{\pi}{2}\right) \tag{3.1a}$$

where

$$\gamma_o = \frac{\frac{\pi m}{2} + 2h \tan \alpha + \frac{2r_c}{\cos \alpha}}{2R_o} \tag{3.1b}$$

and m is the module of the gear.

The width of the weakest section S_F is given as Equation 3.2.

$$S_F = 2R_o \cos\left(\delta + \frac{\pi}{6}\right) - 2\cos\frac{\pi}{6}\left(\frac{h}{\cos\delta} + r_c \cos\beta\right) \qquad (3.2)$$

The fillet radius ρ_F can be written as Equation 3.3.

$$\rho_F = \sqrt{\frac{(A^2 + h^2)^3}{A^2 + R_o h + h^2}} + r_c \cos\beta \qquad (3.3)$$

where

$$A = R + \varphi_2 R_o + \left(\Delta + \frac{d_o}{2}\right)\cos\beta \qquad (3.3a)$$

In Equations 3.1, 3.2 and 3.3, three geometric parameters used to determine the critical section, h_F, S_F and ρ_F, are all derived as a function of the helix angle β. They can be changed at the different transverse sections along with the tooth trace owing to the different helix angle β.

REFERENCES

1. Fu, D.Q. 1980. Analysis of the Bending Strength of CATT Cylindrical Gear. Journal of Jilin University of Technology, Vol. 4, No. 21, pp 11-14.
2. Li, Y. 1990. Bending Strength Analysis of CATT Cylindrical Gear. M.S. Thesis, North China Institute of Technology, Taiyuan, China.
3. Fan, C.B. 1979. Gear Strength and Experiment. Mechanical Industry Publisher. Beijing, P.R. China.

4. Moment of Inertia for Critical Section

In CATT gear bending strength analysis, the moment of inertia for the critical section is a property of a shape that is used to predict the bending stress of the tooth. In this Chapter, the moments of inertia of critical section about its horizontal neutral axis x_0x_0 and vertical neutral axis y_0y_0 are calculated. Firstly, the centroid of the critical section is computed by dividing the section into three simpler shapes. Secondly, the moment of inertia for each simpler shape is computed about its centroid axis and then calculating the total moment of inertia by parallel axis theorem.

More details about the calculation procedure and resulted equations are outlined in the following paragraphs.

Figure 4.1 shows a schematic diagram of the critical section at the tooth root fillet, which is determined by the method of Hofer 30° tangential line, as introduced in Chapter 3. A Cartesian coordinate O(X, Y) is attached to the section at O, and axis Y passes through the centroid of the section. These choices get results in the critical section being symmetry about the vertical Y-axis and also the axis Y coinciding with vertical neutral axis y_0y_0. But, the critical section is asymmetry about the horizontal X-axis. The axis X parallels with the horizontal neutral axis x_0x_0.

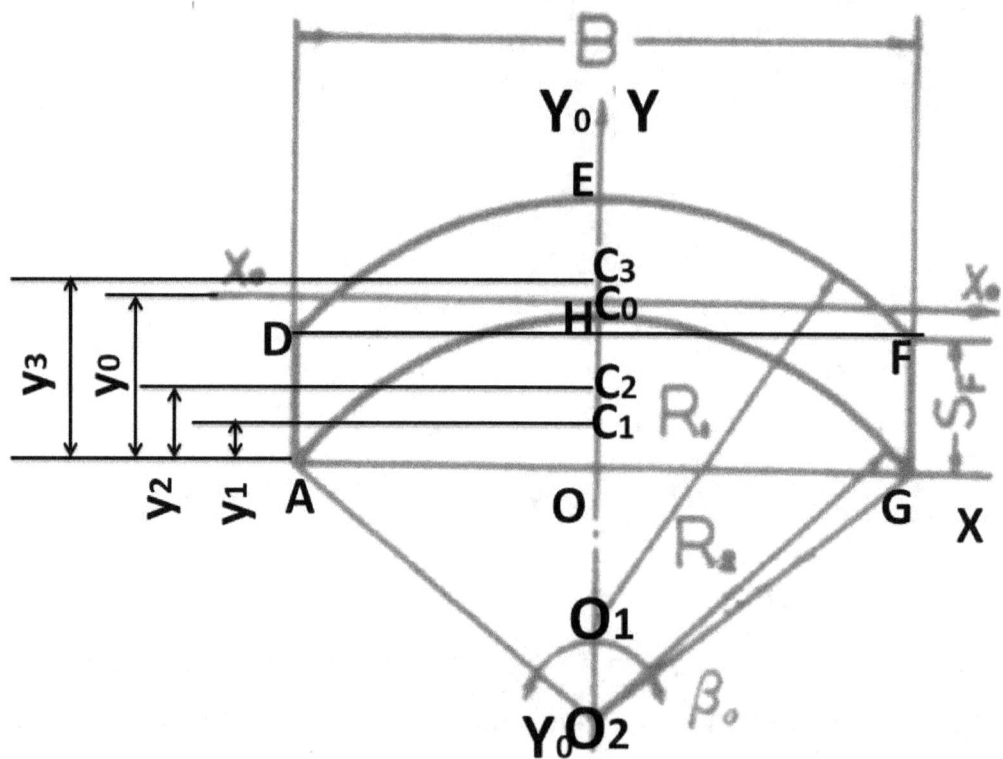

Figure 4.1 Schematic Diagram of a Critical Cross Section at CATT Gear Tooth. The Symbols Used in Chapter 4 are Labeled

4.1 CENTROID OF THE CRITICAL SECTION

For calculating the tooth bending stress, the moment of inertia of critical section about its horizontal neutral axis x_0x_0 and vertical neutral axis y_0y_0 are required. Thus, the centroid of the critical section surrounded by a polygon ADEFGHA, will be needed first. It can be computed by three steps: a) dividing the section into three simpler shapes, which are circular segment AHGOA, rectangle ADFGA and circular segment DEFD, b) computing the area F_i and centroid y_i of each segment, and c) calculating y_0, which is the vertical distance from centroid C_0 to axis X and given as Equation 4.1.

$$y_0 = \frac{\sum y_i F_i}{\sum F_i} \qquad (4.1)$$

where i=1, 2, 3. The areas overlapped between the segments will be assigned by negative signs. The item information for the three segments is described below.

- For the circular segment AHGOA:

y_1 is the vertical distance from its centroid C_1 to axis X and can be calculated by Equation 4.2a.

$$y_1 = 4R\frac{\left(\sin\frac{\beta_0}{2}\right)^3}{3(\beta_0 - \sin\beta_0)} - R\cos\frac{\beta_0}{2} \quad (4.2a)$$

F_1 is the area of the circular segment AHGOA, which can be obtained by subtracting the area of the triangle AGO_2A from the area of the circular sector $AHGO_2A$ as expressed in Equation 4.2b.

$$\begin{aligned}F_1 &= \pi R^2 \frac{\beta_0}{2\pi} - R\sin\frac{\beta_0}{2}R\cos\frac{\beta_0}{2} \\ &= R^2\frac{\beta_0}{2} - \frac{R^2}{2}2\sin\frac{\beta_0}{2}\cos\frac{\beta_0}{2} \\ &= \frac{R^2}{2}(\beta_0 - \sin\beta_0)\end{aligned} \quad (4.2b)$$

- For the rectangle segment ADFGA:

y_2 is the vertical distance from its centroid C_2 to axis X and can be obtained by Equation 4.3a.

$$y_2 = \frac{S_F}{2} \quad (4.3a)$$

F_2 is the area of the rectangle ADFGA and can be calculated by Equation 4.3b.

$$F_2 = BS_F \quad (4.3b)$$

where B is the tooth width of CATT gear.

- For the circular segment DEFD:

y_3 is the vertical distance from its centroid C_3 to axis X. In Chapter 2, the radius of the convex tooth is assumed to equal to one of the concave tooth, which is $R_1=R_2=R$. Hence, the circular segment DEFD is similar to the circular segment AHGOA. There is the same centroid position for two segments. Thus, y_3 can be written as Equation 4.4a.

$$y_3 = y_1 + S_F$$
$$= 4R\frac{\left(\sin\frac{\beta_0}{2}\right)^3}{3(\beta_0 - \sin\beta_0)} - R\cos\frac{\beta_0}{2} + S_F \qquad (4.4a)$$

F_3 is the area of the circular segment DEFD. An essential point here is that this segment has the same size as the area of the circular segment AHGOA F_1. This fact makes the area DEFD F_3 equal to the area AHGOA F_1. Hence, their relationship can be built as Equation 4.4b.

$$F_3 = F_1 \qquad (4.4b)$$

- For the critical section ADEFGHA:

y_0 is the vertical distance from its centroid C_0 to axis X. By unfolding Equation 4.1, it can be expressed as Equation 4.5a.

$$y_0 = \frac{-y_1 F_1 + y_2 F_2 + y_3 F_3}{\sum F_i} \qquad (4.5a)$$

where $\sum F_i$ is the area ADEFGHA F_0, which can be calculated by adding the area DEFD to the area ADFGA and subtracting the area AHGOA, as given in Equation 4.5b.

$$F_0 = \sum F_i = -F_1 + F_2 + F_3$$
$$= -F_1 + BS_F + F_1 \quad (4.5b)$$
$$= BS_F$$

So far, all information has been provided for Equation 4.5a. The vertical distance from the centroid of critical section C_0 to axis X can be calculated by Equation 4.6.

$$y_0 = \frac{-y_1 F_1 + y_2 BS_F + y_3 F_1}{F_0}$$
$$= \frac{-y_1 F_1 + y_2 BS_F + y_3 F_1}{BS_F} \quad (4.6)$$
$$= y_2 + \frac{F_1(y_3 - y_1)}{BS_F}$$

Substituting Equations 4.3a and 4.4a to 4.6, the final Equation of the vertical distance y_0 from the centroid of critical section ADEFGHA C_0 to axis X can be written as Equation 4.7.

$$y_0 = \frac{S_F}{2} + \frac{F_1}{B} \quad (4.7)$$

4.2 MOMENT OF INERTIA FOR THE CRITICAL SECTION

The moment of inertia for the critical section is broken down into two components about its horizontal neutral axis $x_0 x_0$ and vertical neutral axis $y_0 y_0$. It can be calculated by three steps: a) splitting the polygon ADEFGHA into three segments, circular segment AHGOA, rectangle ADFGA, and circular segment DEFD, b) calculating the moment of inertia of individual segment I_{ci} about its centroid axis, and c) calculating the total moment of inertia I_0 by parallel axis theorem as given in Equation 4.8.

$$I_0 = \sum (I_{ci} + F_i d_i^2) \quad (4.8)$$

where i=1, 2, 3. If segments overlapped between the parts, Ic_i and F_i will be assigned by negative signs. d_i is the vertical distance from the individual centroid of the segment to the neutral axis.

Firstly, the moment of inertia I_{x0x0} for the critical section for bending around the x_0x_0 axis can be expressed as Equation 4.9.

$$I_{x0x0} = \sum(I_{Cix} + F_i d_{ix}^2) \tag{4.9}$$

where the items of Ic_{ix}, F_i and d_{ix} for three segments are explained below.

- For the circular segment AHGOA:

Ic_{1x} is the moment of inertia of the circular segment AHGOA about its horizontal centroid axis.

d_{1x} is the vertical distance from its centroid C_1 to the neutral axis x_0x_0 as given by Equation 4.10.

$$d_{1x} = C_0C_1 = y_0 - y_1 \tag{4.10}$$

- For the rectangle segment ADFGA:

Ic_{2x} is the moment of inertia of the rectangle segment ADFGA about its own horizontal centroid axis, which can be calculated by the moment of the inertia equation of a rectangle shape. The result is given in Equation 4.11.

$$I_{C2x} = \frac{BS_F^3}{12} \tag{4.11}$$

d_{2x} is the vertical distance from its centroid C_2 to the neutral axis x_0x_0. By Equation 4.7, it can be expressed as Equation 4.12.

$$\begin{aligned} d_{2x} &= C_0C_2 = y_0 - y_2 \\ &= \frac{S_F}{2} + \frac{F_1}{B} - \frac{S_F}{2} = \frac{F_1}{B} \end{aligned} \tag{4.12}$$

- For the circular segment DEFD:

I_{C3x} is the moment of inertia of the circular segment DEFD about its horizontal centroid axis. In Figure 4.1, the circular segment AHGOA is similar to the circular segment DEFD, therefore

$$I_{C1x} = I_{C3x} \tag{4.13}$$

d_{3x} is the vertical distance from its centroid C_3 to the neutral axis x_0x_0, as shown in Equation 4.14.

$$d_{3x} = C_0 C_3 = y_0 - y_3 \tag{4.14}$$

Substituting all the information of three segments I_{Cix}, F_i and d_{ix} into Equation 4.9 and the moment of inertia for the critical section I_{x0x0} is computed by Equation 4.15.

$$\begin{aligned} I_{x0x0} &= \Sigma(I_{Cix} + F_i d_{ix}^2) \\ &= -I_{C1x} - F_1(y_0 - y_1)^2 + I_{C2x} + F_2(y_0 - y_2)^2 + I_{C3x} + F_3(y_0 - y_3)^2 \\ &= F_1[(y_0 - y_3)^2 - (y_0 - y_1)^2] + \frac{BS_F^3}{12} + \frac{F_1^2 S_F}{B} \end{aligned} \tag{4.15}$$

Secondly, recalling Equation 4.8, the moment of inertia for the critical section I_{y0y0} for bending around the y_0y_0 axis can be expressed as Equation 4.16.

$$I_{y0y0} = \Sigma(I_{Ciy} + F_i d_{iy}^2) \tag{4.16}$$

The moment of inertia for the critical section I_{y0y0} is more accessible to calculate than the I_{x0x0} because the critical section presents symmetry about the vertical Y-axis. Referring to Figure 4.1, it notes the axis Y coincides with neutral axis y_0y_0. Therefore, in Equation 4.16, $d_{iy}=0$, and it is simplified as Equation 4.17.

$$I_{y0y0} = \Sigma I_{Ciy} \tag{4.17}$$

where the items of Ic_{iy} for three segments are explained below.

- For the circular segment AHGOA:

Ic_{1y} is the moment of inertia of the circular segment AHGOA about its vertical centroid axis.

- For the rectangle segment ADFGA:

Ic_{2y} is the moment of inertia of the rectangle segment ADFGA about its vertical centroid axis, which can be calculated by the moment of the inertia equation of a rectangle shape. The result is given in Equation 4.18.

$$I_{C2y} = \frac{BS_F^3}{12} \qquad (4.18)$$

- For the circular segment DEFD:

Ic_{3y} is the moment of inertia of the circular segment DEFD about its vertical centroid axis.

In Figure 4.1, the circular segment AHGOA is similar to the circular segment DEFD, therefore

$$I_{C1y} = I_{C3y} \qquad (4.19)$$

Substituting all the information of three segments Ic_{iy} into Equation 4.16 and the moment of inertia for critical section Iy_0y_0 is obtained by Equation 4.20.

$$\begin{aligned} I_{y0y0} &= -I_{C1y} + I_{C2y} + I_{C3y} \\ &= \frac{BS_F^3}{12} \end{aligned} \qquad (4.20)$$

5. Stress Estimations on the Critical Section

In this Chapter, works from Chapters 2-4 are brought together in establishing equations of component stresses and equivalent stresses on the critical section. Initially, the bending stress, normal stress and shear stress are modeled. Then, by combining the bending stress with normal stress, the equivalent bending stress is obtained; and by combining the component shear stresses, the equivalent shear stress is created. Finally, integration of the equivalent bending stress and the equivalent shear stress leads to the general equivalent stress.

Figure 5.1 shows a schematic diagram of a critical section for evaluating component stresses and equivalent stresses on the critical section of the CATT gear tooth. The symbols used in Chapter 5 are indicated there. A local Cartesian coordinate o(x, y) is attached to the critical section with the origin o at the centroid C_0. Horizontal axis x coincides with the horizontal neutral axis $x_0 x_0$; and the vertical axis y coincides with the vertical neutral axis $y_0 y_0$.

5.1 ESTIMATION OF COMPONENT STRESS ON THE CRITICAL SECTION

The component stresses applied on the critical section can be caused by the tangential force, radial force and axial force, respectively. Each component force may cause bending stress, normal stress and shear stress on the critical section. The detailed stress generation and calculation are discussed below.

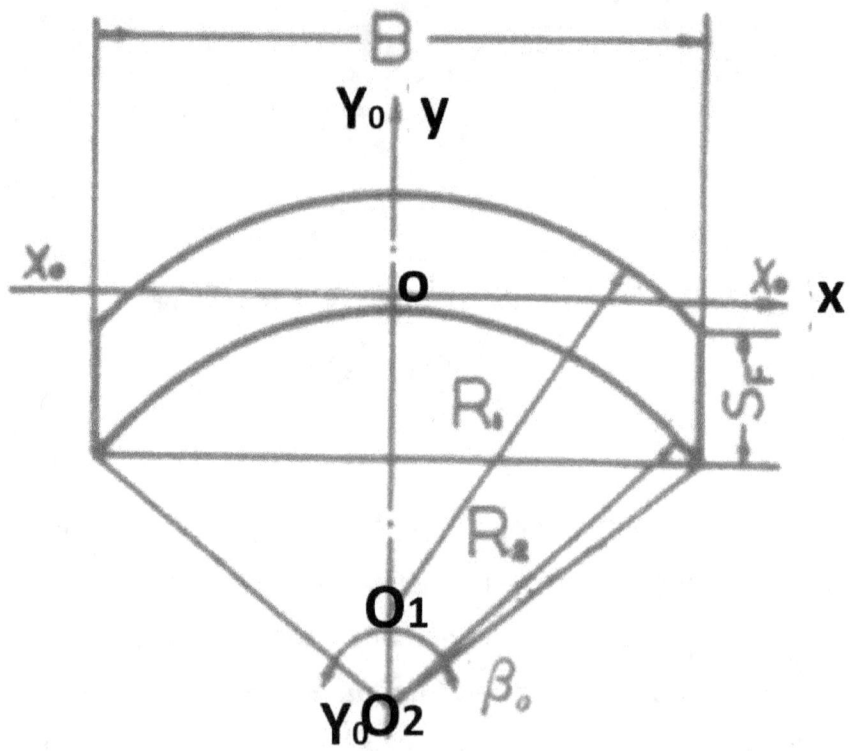

Figure 5.1 A Schematic Diagram of Critical Section of CATT Gear Tooth for Indicating the Symbols Used in Chapter 5

It is customary to compute the bending stress on the assumption that the gear tooth is a cantilever beam. If classic formula, $\sigma=-My/I$, (Gere and Timoshenko, 1997) for bending stress is used, the result at best is only approximate. Accuracy cannot be secured because the tooth is short and thick and nonuniform in the critical section. It must be remembered that the derivation of the equation for bending stress assumed along a thin beam of the constant cross-section. Also, for concentrated load, the formula is valid only at point considering distance away from the point of application of the force.

Nevertheless, it is customary to use the classic formula for determining the bending stress in a beam under simple bending (Richard et al., 2011)

On the critical section of CATT gear tooth, the tangential component force P_t produces a bending moment with respect to axis x, which can be written as

$M_{xPt}=P_t h_F$. The moment produces an asymmetric bending stress σ_1 over the critical section because the critical section is asymmetric about the horizontal neutral axis $x_0 x_0$. The moment of inertia for the critical section I_{x0x0} is introduced in Equation 4.15. In terms of the classic bending stress formula, the bending stress on the critical section σ_1 is expressed as Equation 5.1.

$$\sigma_1 = \frac{-P_t h_F y}{I_{x0x0}} \qquad (5.1)$$

The radial component force P_r produces uniform normal stress σ_c over the critical section. The average normal stress due to normal loading is $\sigma_c = P_r/F_0$ (Hibbeler, 2004). The area of the section $F_0 = BS_F$ is given by Equation 4.5b. The radial component force P_r behaves as a compressive style. Thus, the normal stress behaves as compressive stress σ_c on the critical section, which is expressed as Equation 5.2.

$$\sigma_c = \frac{P_r}{BS_F} \qquad (5.2)$$

Substituting Equation 2.4b (formulas of radial force P_r) in Equation 5.2, the final compressive stress σ_c is expressed as Equation 5.3.

$$\sigma_c = \frac{P_t \tan \alpha_n}{\beta_0 BS_F} \ln \frac{1 + \sin \frac{\beta_0}{2}}{1 - \sin \frac{\beta_0}{2}} \qquad (5.3)$$

So far, combined normal stress σ_2 applied on the critical section is produced by the bending stress σ_1 due to the bending loading and the compressive stress σ_c due to the radial loading. The vectors of both stresses are normal to the critical section. The summation of Equations 5.1b and 5.3 leads to the resulted normal stress σ_2 as given in Equation 5.4.

$$\sigma_2 = \sigma_1 - \sigma_2 = \frac{-P_t h_F y}{I_{x0x0}} - \frac{P_t \tan \alpha_n}{\beta_0 B S_F} \ln \frac{1 + \sin \frac{\beta_0}{2}}{1 - \sin \frac{\beta_0}{2}}$$

$$= \frac{-P_t h_F y}{I_{x0x0}} - \frac{P_t \tan \alpha_n}{\beta_0 B S_F} \ln \frac{1 + \varphi}{1 - \varphi} \quad (5.4)$$

where $\varphi = \sin(\beta_0/2)$.

The radial component force P_r also produces a bending moment M_{xPr} over the critical section around axis x. The moment produces an asymmetric bending stress σ_3 over the critical section because the critical section is asymmetric about the horizontal neutral axis x_0x_0. Integrating the distributed bending moment $p_r y$ along the tooth trace obtains the total bending moment M_{xPr}. The moment of inertia for the critical section I_{x0x0} is given in Equation 4.15. Employing the classic bending stress formula $\sigma_3 = M_{xPr} y / I_{x0x0}$, the bending stress σ_3 on the critical section is given in Equation 5.5.

$$\sigma_3 = \frac{-M_{xPr} y}{I_{x0x0}} = \frac{-P_t y \tan \alpha_n}{\beta_0 I_{x0x0}} \left(R\beta_0 - C \ln \frac{1 + \varphi}{1 - \varphi} \right) \quad (5.5)$$

where constant C is defined by Equation 5.5a.

$$C = -R \cos \frac{\beta_0}{2} - \left(y_0 - \frac{S_F - S_a}{2} \right) \quad (5.5a)$$

The distributed axial force p_a produces two equal but opposite bending moments M_y on the critical section with respect to the axis y. The moments produce two symmetric bending stresses σ_4 over the critical section because the critical section is symmetric about the vertical neutral axis y_0y_0. Using the classic bending formula, the bending stress σ_4 can be derived from Equation 5.6.

$$\sigma_4 = \frac{-M_y x}{I_{y0y0}} \quad (5.6)$$

It notes that the total axial force in the positive x-direction is equal but opposite to one in the negative x-direction, which is denoted by symbol P_{ahalf}. Integrating the distributed axial force (see Equation 2.7) along with the tooth trace from zero to $\beta_0/2$, the axial force P_{ahalf} can be given in Equation 5.6a.

$$P_{ahalf} = \int_0^{\frac{\beta_o}{2}} p_a\, R d\beta = -\frac{P_t}{\beta_0} \ln \cos \frac{\beta_0}{2} \tag{5.6a}$$

Hence, the bending moments M_y can be obtained by Equation 5.6b.

$$M_y = -\frac{P_t h_F}{\beta_0} \ln \cos \frac{\beta_0}{2} \tag{5.6b}$$

The moment of inertia for the critical section I_{y0y0} is given in Equation 4.20. Substituting Equations 4.20 and 5.6b in 5.6, the resulted bending stress σ_4 on the critical section can be written as Equation 5.7.

$$\sigma_4 = \frac{12 P_t h_F x}{\beta_0 S_F B^3} \ln \cos \frac{\beta_0}{2} \tag{5.7}$$

The tangential force P_t produces a shear stress τ_1 over the critical section. The direction of the shear stress parallels axis y. The genetic formula to calculate average shear stress is shear force per unit area (Hibbeler, 2004). Therefore, the tooth shear stress τ_1 can be expressed as $\tau_1 = P_t/F_0$, where F_0 is the area of the section and can be written as $F_0 = BS_F$ by Equation 4.5b. The result is given in Equation 5.8a.

$$\tau_1 = \frac{P_t}{BS_F} \tag{5.8a}$$

The distributed axial force p_a produces a uniform shear stress τ_2 over the critical section, which parallels axis x and is symmetric to the axis y. The shear stress in positive x side is equal but opposite to one in negative x side. In terms of the genetic shear stress formula, the average shear stress τ_2 can be defined as

$\tau_2 = P_{ahalf}/F_{0half}$, where P_{ahalf} is given by Equation 5.6a; and F_{0half} is the half area of the section $F_{0half}=F_0/2=BS_F/2$ (see Equation 4.5b). The resulted shear stress τ_2 can be expressed as Equation 5.8b.

$$\tau_2 = \frac{2P_t}{\beta_0 BS_F} \ln \cos \frac{\beta_0}{2} \tag{5.8b}$$

5.2 ESTIMATION OF EQUIVALENT STRESS ON THE CRITICAL SECTION

The equivalent stresses on the critical section can be obtained by the combination of the bending stress, normal stress and shear stress on the critical section. The details about the equivalent stress generation and calculation are addressed below.

The equivalent shear stress τ applied on the critical section can be calculated by combining shear stresses τ_1 with τ_2. It notes that the direction of the vector of shear stress τ_1 is orthogonal to the vector of the shear stress τ_2. Thus, the magnitude of the sum of two stresses can be expressed as Equation 5.9a.

$$\tau = \sqrt{\tau_1^2 + \tau_2^2} \tag{5.9a}$$

Substituting Equations 5.8a and 5.8b to Equation 5.9a leads Equation 5.9b.

$$\tau = \frac{P_t}{BS_F} \sqrt{1 + \frac{4}{\beta_0^2} \left(\ln \cos \frac{\beta_0}{2} \right)^2} \tag{5.9b}$$

Employing the strength theory of gear (Fan, 1979), equivalent stress σ_5 applied on the critical section is defined as the combination of the bending stress σ_1 and the equivalent shear stress τ. General equivalent stress on the critical section is written as Equation 5.10a.

$$\sigma_5 = \sqrt{\sigma_1^2 + (2.5\tau)^2} \tag{5.10a}$$

where 2.5 is the shear stress factor. Substituting Equations 5.1a and 5.9b in Equation 5.10a, the final expression of the equivalent stress σ_5 is written as 5.10b.

$$\sigma_5 = P_t \sqrt{\left(\frac{h_F y}{I_{x0x0}}\right)^2 + 2.5^2 \frac{1 + \frac{4}{\beta_0^2}\left(\ln\cos\frac{\beta_0}{2}\right)^2}{B^2 S_F^2}} \tag{5.10b}$$

Equivalent stress σ_6 applied on the critical section is defined as the combination of σ_2 (bending stress plus compressive stress) and the shear stress τ, in terms of the strength theory of gear (Fan, 1979). General equivalent stress on the critical section is expressed in Equation 5.11a.

$$\sigma_6 = \sqrt{\sigma_2^2 + (2.5\tau)^2} \tag{5.11a}$$

Substituting Equations 5.4 and 5.9b to Equation 5.11a, the resulted equivalent stress σ_6 can be written as Equation 5.11b.

$$\sigma_6 = P_t \sqrt{\left(\frac{h_F y}{I_{x0x0}} + \frac{\tan\alpha_n}{\beta_0 B S_F}\ln\frac{1+\varphi}{1-\varphi}\right)^2 + 2.5^2 \frac{1 + \frac{4}{\beta_0^2}\left(\ln\cos\frac{\beta_0}{2}\right)^2}{B^2 S_F^2}} \tag{5.11b}$$

REFERENCES

1. Gere, J.M. and Timoshenko, S.P. 1997. Mechanics of Materials, PWS Publishing Company, USA.

2. Richard, G., Budynas, J. and Nisbett, K. 2011. Shigley's Mechanical Engineering Design,"9th Ed., The McGraw Hill Companies, New York.
3. Hibbeler, R.C. 2004. Mechanics of Materials. New Jersey USA: Pearson Education. pp. 32. ISBN 0-13-191345-X.
4. Fan, C.B. 1979. Gear Strength and Experiment. Mechanical Industry Publisher. Beijing, P.R. China.

6. One Case Study of Tooth Stresses on the Root Fillet

In this case study, CATT gear tooth stresses (σ_1 to σ_6) are calculated along the tooth trace on the root fillet at six selected positions. Stress Equations established in Chapter 5 are brought together for comparison purposes. For the six stresses, the individual stress distribution is exhibited and analyzed. And the maximum stress is predicted.

The basic CATT gear parameters for calculating stress distributions along the tooth trace at the root fillet are specified as: number of teeth is Z=19, module is m=5 mm, pressure angle (or profile angle of the cutting tool) is $\alpha=20°$, reference radius is R=69.5mm, tooth width factor is $\varphi=0.72$ and central angle is $\beta_0 =92°$.

The loading condition is specified as: a tangential force of P_t=1000N is applied on the top of the concave tooth.

Figure 6.1 shows a schematic diagram of the critical section of the CATT gear tooth labeled the selected six positions. The first five position points of 0, 1, 2, 3, and 4, are uniformly distributed along the concave tooth root fillet from the middle transverse section to the left side; and the last point of 5 is located on the convex tooth root fillet at the middle transverse section. Figures 6.2a-f show six individual stress distributions along the tooth trace on the root fillet at the points of 0, 1,..., 5.

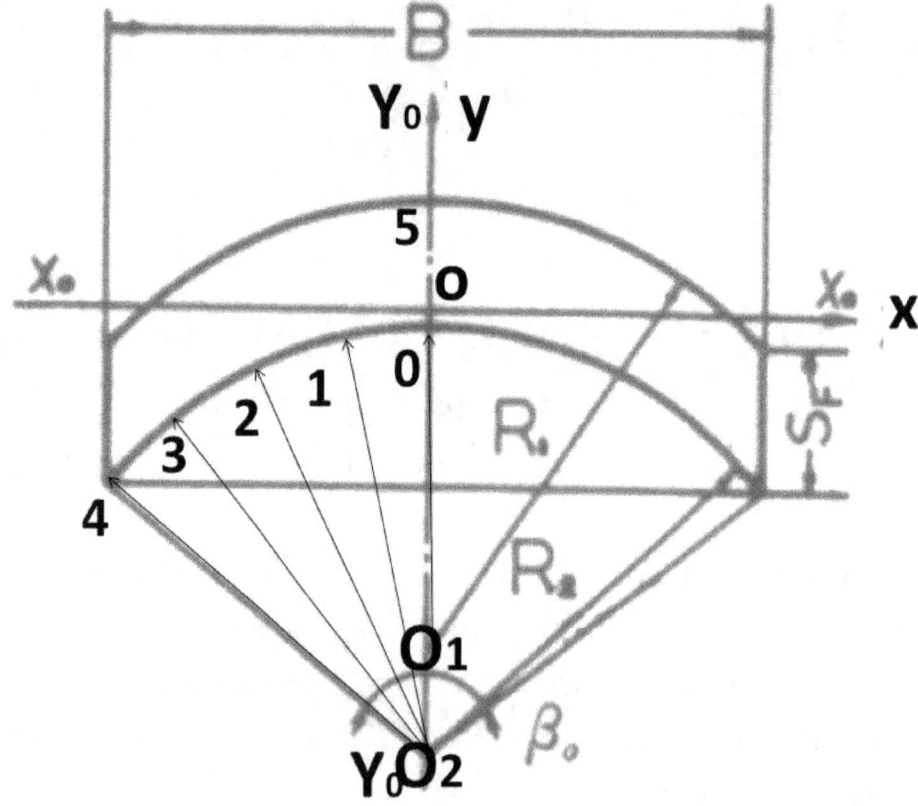

Figure 6.1 A Schematic Diagram of Critical Section of CATT Gear Tooth Labeled the Six Positions at Points 0, 1,..., 5

Figure 6.2a shows the bending stress σ_1 distributed at points of 0, 1,..., 5 (calculated by Equation 5.1a). At the concave tooth root fillet, the stress σ_1 displays tension stress and increases from points 0 to 4. The minimum stress of 1×10^4 Pa occurs at the center point 0, and the maximum stress of 4.09×10^6 Pa does at the side point 4. At the convex tooth root fillet, the stress σ_1 at center point 5 displays compressive stress with the negative value of -2.6×10^5 Pa. Reviewing the stress σ_1 from points 0 to 5, it notes that the maximum magnitude of 4.09×10^6 Pa occurs at the left side point 4. Since the critical section is symmetric about the vertical neutral axis y_0y_0, it can figure out that the maximum magnitude locates at the two sides on the root fillet of the concave tooth.

Figure 6.2b shows the combined normal stress σ_2 distributed at points of 0, 1,..., 5 (calculated by Equation 5.4). At the concave tooth root fillet, stress σ_2 depicts the compressive stress with the negative value decreasing from points 0 to 2, and then the tension stress with the positive value increasing from points 3 to 4. The minimum stress magnitude of $|-1.4 \times 10^5$ Pa$|$ occurs at the center point 0 and the maximum stress of 3.69×10^6 Pa does at the left side point 4. At the convex tooth root fillet, the stress σ_2 at center point 5 depicts compressive stress with the negative value of -6.5×10^5 Pa.

Different to σ_1, for σ_2, the compressive stress takes domination from points 0 to 2. This is because σ_2 is the sum of the bending stress σ_1 and the compressive stress σ_c (see Equation 5.4).

Similar to σ_1, the maximum σ_2 of 3.69×10^6 Pa locates at the left side point 4. Therefore, it can conduct that the maximum magnitude occurs at the two sides on the root fillet of the concave tooth due to the symmetry of the critical section about the vertical neutral axis $y_0 y_0$.

Figure 6.2c shows the bending stress σ_3 distributed at points of 0, 1,..., 5 (calculated by Equation 5.5). At the concave tooth root fillet, stress σ_3 exhibits the compressive stress with the negative value decreasing from points 0 to 4. The minimum stress magnitude of $|-6 \times 10^4$ Pa$|$ appears at the center point 0 and the maximum one of $|-1.44 \times 10^6$ Pa$|$ does at the left side point 4. At the convex tooth root fillet, the stress σ_3 at center point 5 exhibits tension stress with the positive value of 9.2×10^4 Pa.

Overviewing the stress σ_3 from points 0 to 5, it notes that the maximum magnitude of $|-1.44 \times 10^6$ Pa$|$ locates at the left side point 4. It can conclude that the maximum magnitude presents at the two sides on the root fillet of the concave tooth due to the symmetry of the critical section about the vertical neutral axis $y_0 y_0$.

Figure 6.2d shows the bending stress σ_4 distributed at points of 0, 1,..., 5 (calculated by Equation 5.7). At the concave tooth root fillet, stress σ_4 gives the tension stress with the positive value increasing from points 0 to 4. The minimum stress magnitude of 0 Pa happens at the center point 0 and the maximum one of 1.3×10^5 Pa does at the left side point 4. At the convex tooth root fillet, the stress σ_4 at center point 5 gives zero stress, because this point is located on the bending vertical neutral axis $y_0 y_0$.

Checking the stress σ_4 from points 0 to 5, it notes that the maximum magnitude of 1.3×10^5 Pa presents at the left side point 4. Therefore, it can conclude that the maximum magnitude presents at the two sides on the root fillet of the concave tooth due to the symmetry of the critical section about the vertical neutral axis $y_0 y_0$.

Figure 6.2e shows the equivalent stress σ_5 distributed at points of 0, 1,..., 5 (calculated by Equation 5.10b). At the concave tooth root fillet, stress σ_5 demonstrates the positive stress with the value increasing from points 0 to 4. The minimum stress magnitude of 2.5×10^6 Pa appears at the center point 0 and the maximum one of 4.83×10^6 Pa does at the left side point 4. At the convex tooth root fillet, the stress σ_5 at center point 5 demonstrates the positive stress of 2.6×10^6 Pa.

Reviewing stress σ_5 from points 0 to 5, it notes that the maximum magnitude of 4.83×10^6 Pa presents at the left side point 4. Therefore, it can conclude that the maximum magnitude presents at the two sides on the root fillet of the concave tooth due to the symmetry of the critical section about the vertical neutral axis $y_0 y_0$.

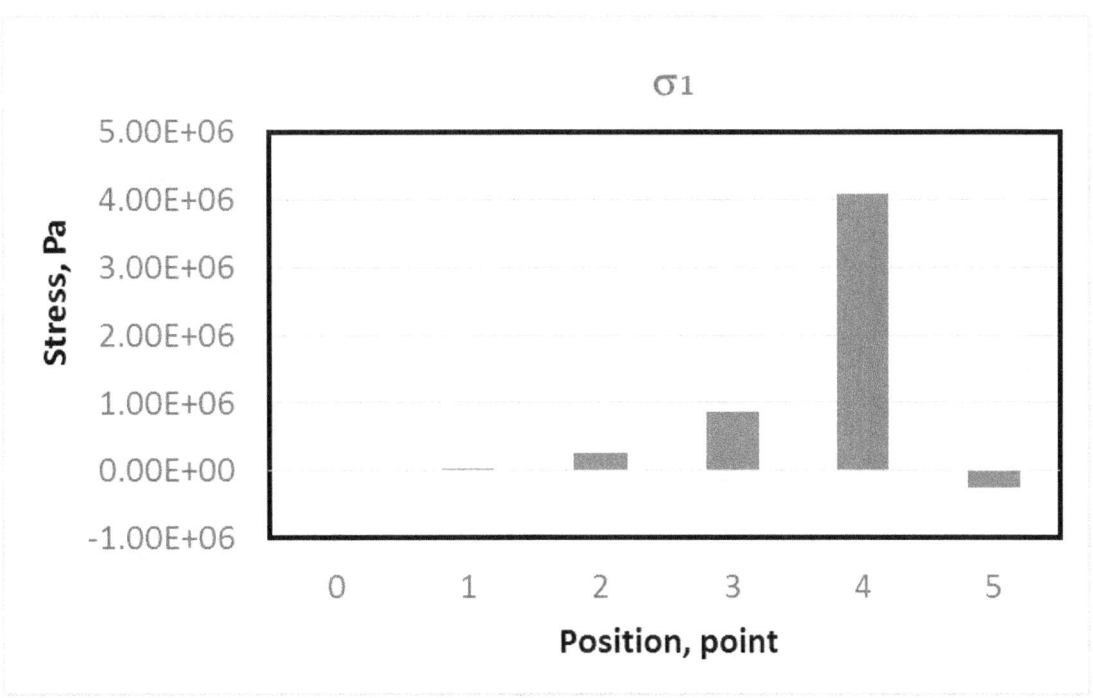

(a) Bending Stress σ_1

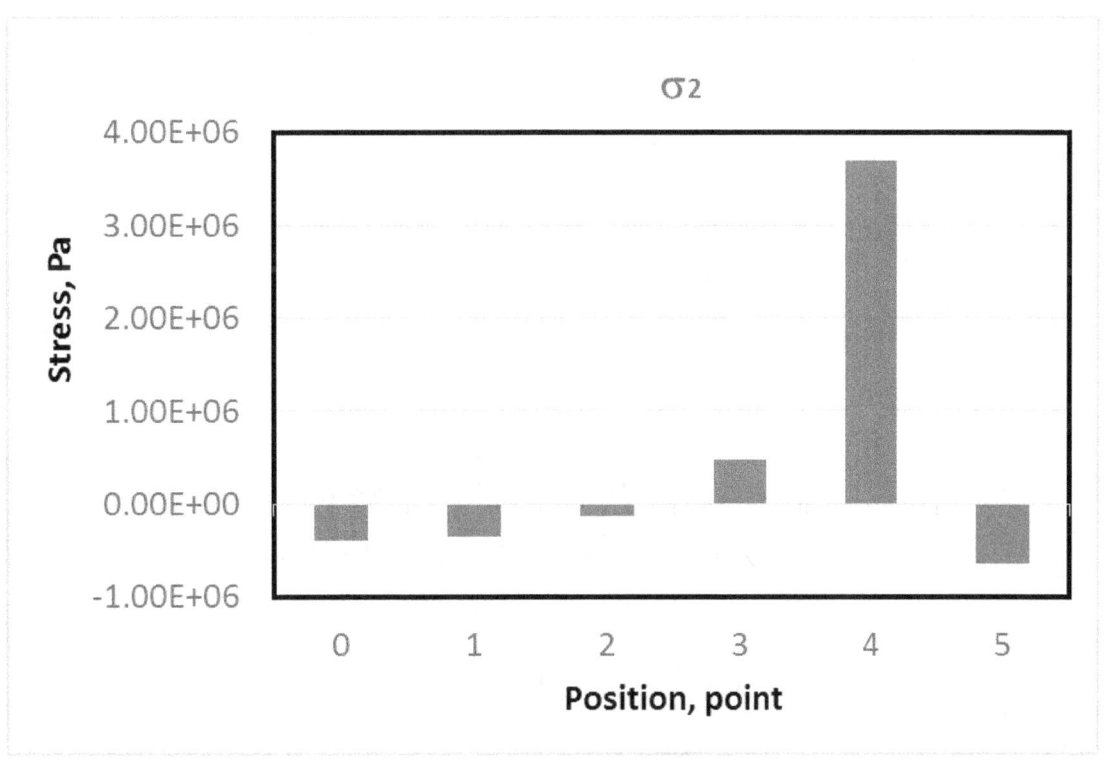

(b) Combined Stress σ_2

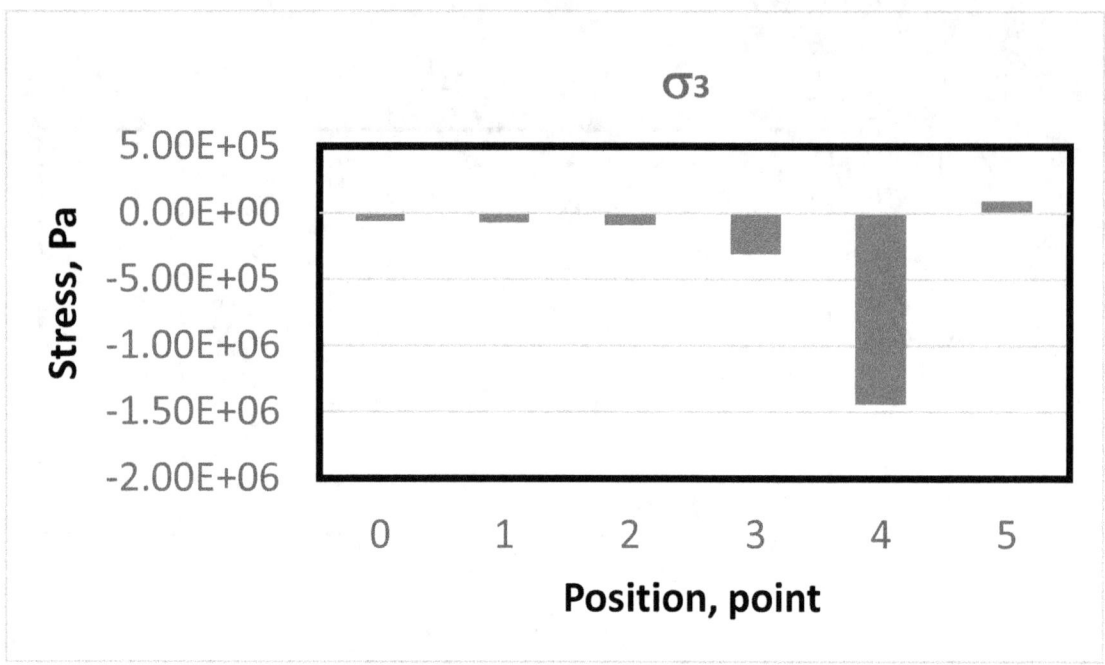

(c) Bending Stress σ_3

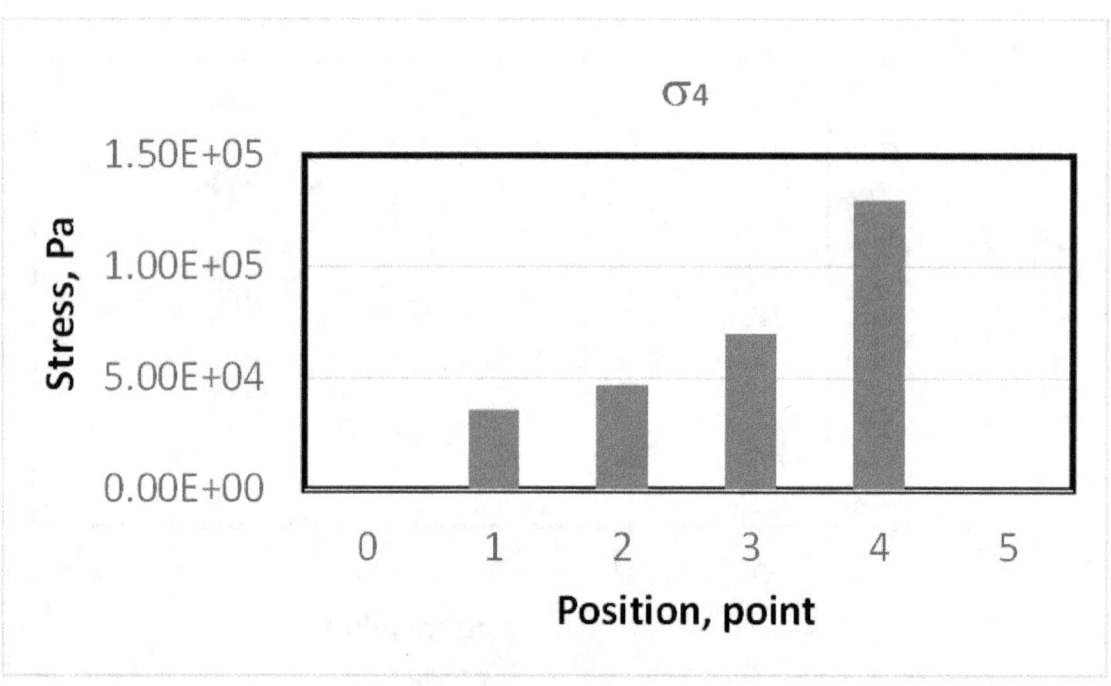

(d) Bending Stress σ_4

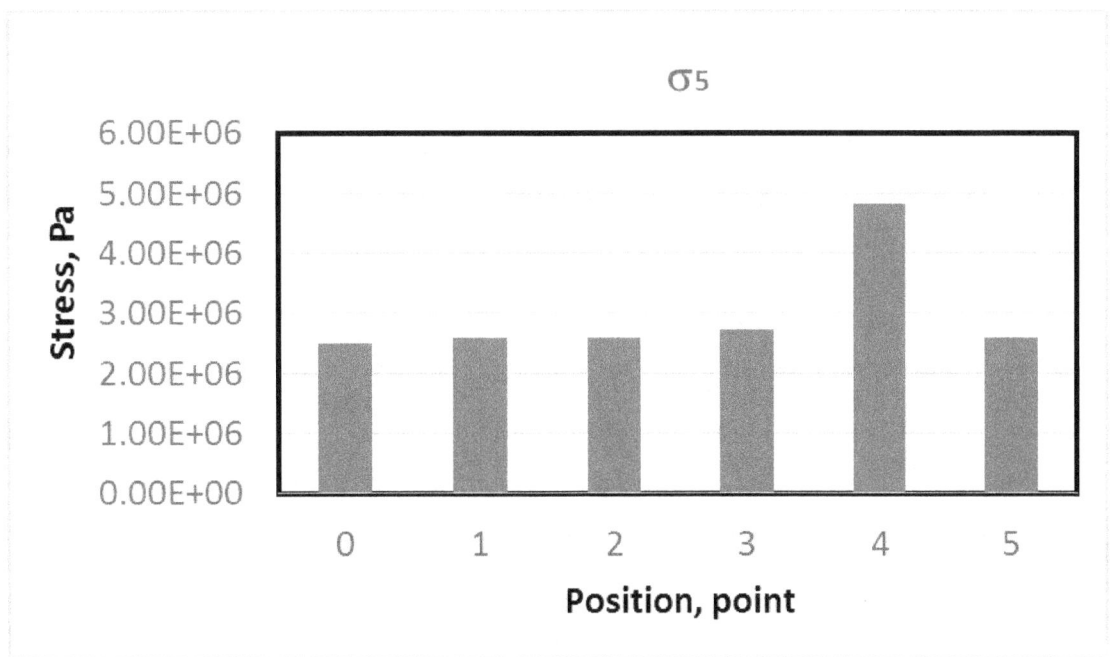

(e) Equivalent Stress σ_5

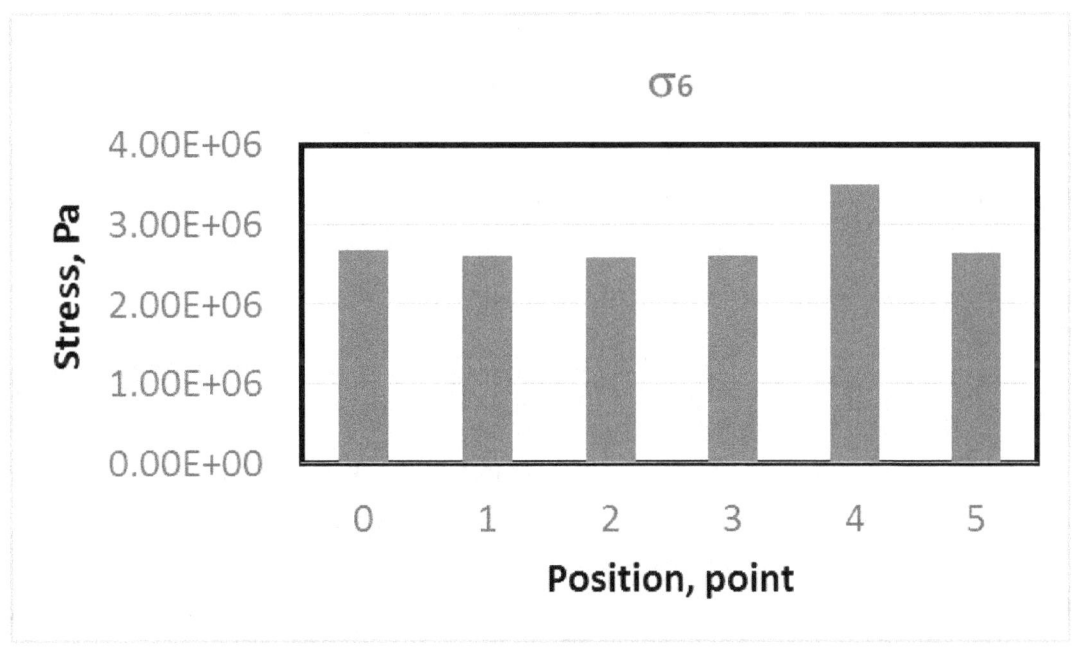

(f) Equivalent Stress σ_6

Figures 6.2 Six Individual Stress Distributions at Points of 0, 1,..., 5

Figure 6.2e shows the equivalent stress σ_6 distributed at points of 0, 1,..., 5 (calculated by Equation 5.11b). At the concave tooth root fillet, the stress σ_6 presents the positive stress with the value fluctuating between 2.59×10^6 and

2.67x10^6 Pa from points 0 to 3, and then reaching 3.51x10^6 Pa at point 4. The minimum stress magnitude of 2.59x10^6 Pa presents at point 2 and the maximum one of 3.51x10^6 Pa does on the left side at point 4. At the convex tooth root fillet, the stress σ_6 at center point 5 presents positive stress of 2.64x10^6 Pa.

Reviewing stress σ_6 from points 0 to 5, it notes that the maximum magnitude of 3.51x10^6 Pa appears at the left side point 4. Since the critical section is symmetric about the vertical neutral axis $y_0 y_0$, it can conclude that the maximum magnitude presents at the two sides on the root fillet of the concave tooth.

In general, the analysis results show that for concave tooth, the stress magnitude mostly increases from the middle transverse section to the two sides of the tooth length. The maximum stress occurs at the two sides on the root fillet of the concave tooth. But, the change of the maximum stress for the convex tooth opposes one for the concave tooth (Li, 1990). The maximum stress occurs at the middle transverse section on the root fillet of the convex tooth.

REFERENCES

1. Li, Y. 1990. Test and Analysis on Bending Stress of Line Contact CATT Gear. Master Degree Thesis, North University of China, China.

7. Bending Stress Distributions along the Tooth Trace at Tooth Root Fillet

In this case study, the bending stress distributions along the tooth trace at the root fillet are predicted for CATT gear. The effort of the module, number of teeth, and tooth width factor on the bending stress is analyzed according to the load applied on the top of the concave tooth and convex tooth, respectively.

Equation 5.1 is used to calculate the bending stress at tooth root fillet and is rewritten as Equation 7.1.

$$\sigma = \frac{-P_t h_F y}{I_{x0x0}} = \frac{P_t}{Bm} Y_{Fa} \tag{7.1}$$

where Y_{Fa} is the form factor and is given as Equation 7.1a.

$$Y_{Fa} = \frac{-Bm h_F y}{I_{x0x0}} \tag{7.1a}$$

Y_{Fa} is the functions of tooth shape and therefore varies with the module, number of teeth, and tooth width factor in the gear. The basic CATT gear tooth parameters in the middle transverse section are given in Table 7.1.

Table 7.1 Basic CATT Gear Parameters at Middle Transverse Section (Li and Zhao, 1997)

| Number of | Module | Pressure | Tooth | Reference | Tooth Width |

Teeth (Z)	(m)	Angle (α)	Width (B)	Radius (R)	Factor (φ)
19	5	20°	100mm	69mm	0.72

The loading condition is specified as: a tangential force of P_t is applied on the top of the concave tooth or convex tooth, respectively. The loading torque of the gear is specified as 50Nm. Equation 2.1 is employed to calculate P_t and can be rewritten as Equation 7.2.

$$P_t = \frac{2T}{d_a - S_a \tan \alpha_n} \tag{7.2}$$

where T is the torque generated on the gear, d_a is the diameter of addendum circle, S_a is the tooth thickness at addendum circle, and α_n is the pressure angle at addendum circle.

Figures 7.1-7.3 show the stress distributions along the tooth trace at the root fillet as the load applied on the top of the concave tooth and convex tooth, respectively. Respective stress distributions on the concave tooth and convex tooth are plotted by varying three parameters: module, number of teeth, and tooth width factor. The details are addressed in the following paragraphs.

Varying Module: Figures 7.1a-d display the stress and helix angle σ-β histories for three given modules: 3, 5, and 7, when other parameters given in Table 7.1 are identical. According to two kinds of loading conditions, the discussion is separated into the following two groups.

Group I: As the load is applied on the top of the concave tooth, the stress distributions at the root fillets of the concave tooth and convex tooth are represented in Figures 7.1a-b, respectively. For each curve, the stress distribution is symmetric to the middle transverse section, and the stress decreases from the two sides to the middle transverse section. The maximum stress occurs at the two sides, and minimum stress occurs in the middle transverse section.

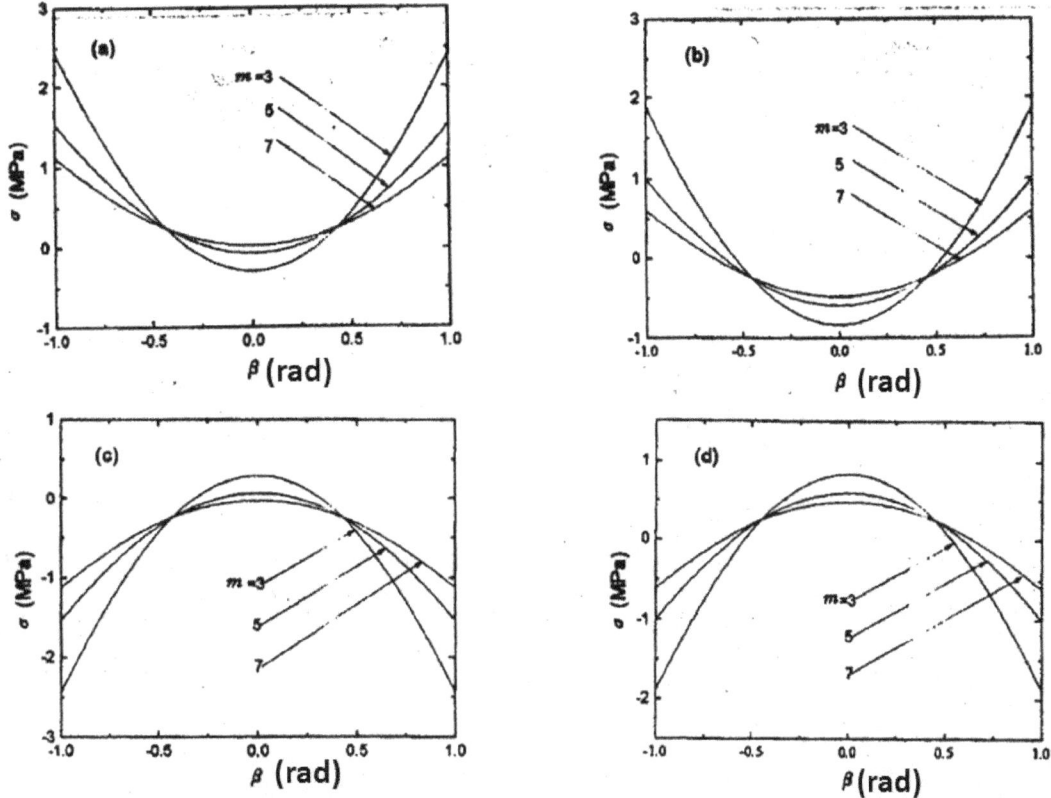

Figure 7.1 Stress and Helix Angle σ-β Histories for Three Given Modules at:
(a) the root fillet of convcave tooth with the load applied on the top of concave tooth
(b) the root fillet of convex tooth with the load applied on the top of concave tooth
(c) the root fillet of convcave tooth with the load applied on the top of convex tooth
(d) the root fillet of convex tooth with the load applied on the top of convex tooth

For the three curves, at the two sides, the smaller the module is, the bigger the stress is; at the section of β=0.45 rad, the module does not affect the stress (σ=constant); and at the middle transverse section, the smaller the module is, the smaller the stress is.

Comparing two curves in Figure 7.1a and 7.1b, which have a same module, it notes that for a given transverse section, the stress at the root fillet of the concave tooth is bigger than on the convex tooth.

Group II: As the load is applied on the top of the convex tooth, the stress distributions at the root fillets of the concave tooth and convex tooth are presented in Figures 7.1c-d, respectively. For each curve, the stress distribution is symmetric to the middle transverse section, and the stress increases from the two sides to the middle transverse section. The maximum stress occurs in the middle transverse section, and minimum stress occurs at two sides.

For the three curves, at the two sides, the smaller the module is, the smaller the stress is; at the section of $\beta=0.45$ rad, the module does not affect the stress (σ=constant); and at the middle transverse section, the smaller the module is, the bigger the stress is. This tendency is opposite to the one in Figure 7.1a-b.

Comparing two curves in Figures 7.1c and 7.1d, which have the same module, it notes that for a given transverse section (β), the stress magnitude $|\sigma|$ at the root fillet of the concave tooth is bigger than on the convex tooth.

Therefore, in Figure 7.1, the stress increases from the middle transverse section to two ends of tooth length when the load is applied on the top of the concave tooth. Conversely, when the load is applied on the top of the convex tooth, the stress decreases from the middle transverse section to the two ends of the tooth length.

Varying Number of Teeth: Figures 7.2a-d display the stress and helix angle σ-β histories for four given number of teeth: 19, 30, 50, and 100, when other parameters given in Table 7.1 are fixed. Based on the two types of loading conditions, the discussion is divided into the following two groups.

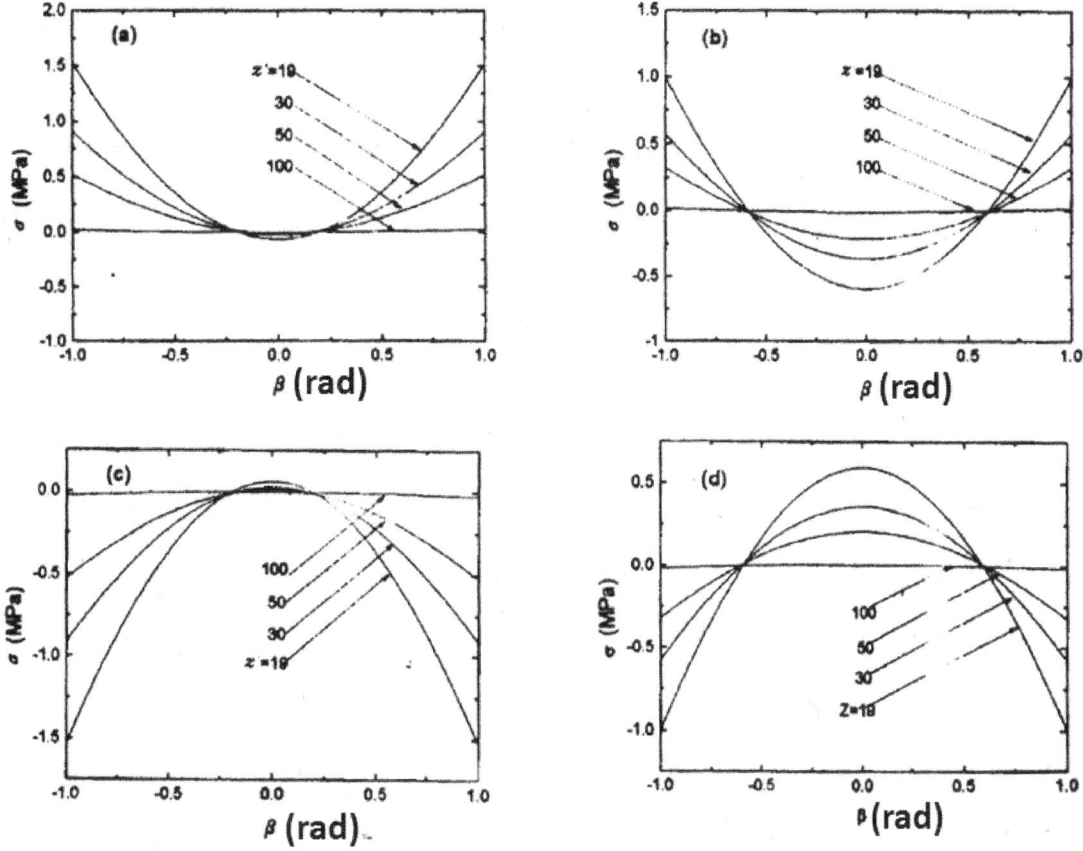

Figure 7.2 Stress and Helix Angle σ-β Histories for Four Given Number of Teeth at:

(a) the root fillet of convcave tooth with the load applied on the top of concave tooth

(b) the root fillet of convex tooth with the load applied on the top of concave tooth

(c) the root fillet of convcave tooth with the load applied on the top of convex tooth

(d) the root fillet of convex tooth with the load applied on the top of convex tooth

Group I: As the load is applied on the top of the concave tooth, the stress distributions at the root fillets of the concave tooth and convex tooth are demonstrated in Figures 7.2a-b, respectively. For each curve, the stress distribution is symmetric to the middle transverse section, and the stress reduces from the two sides to the middle transverse section. The maximum stress appears at the two sides, and minimum stress appears in the middle transverse section.

For the four curves, at the two sides, the less the number of teeth is, the larger the stress is; at the section of $\beta=0.3$ rad, the number of teeth does not affect the stress (σ=constant); and at the middle transverse section, the less the number of teeth is, the less the stress is.

Comparing two curves in Figure 7.2a and 7.2b, which have the same number of teeth, it finds that for a given transverse section, the stress at the root fillet of the concave tooth is larger than on the convex tooth.

Group II: As the load is applied on the top of the convex tooth, the stress distributions at the root fillets of the concave tooth and convex tooth are demonstrated in Figures 7.2c-d, respectively. For each curve, the stress distribution is symmetric to the middle transverse section, and the stress rises from the two sides to the middle transverse section. The maximum stress appears in the middle transverse section, and minimum stress appears at two sides.

For the four curves, at the two sides, the less the number of teeth is, the less the stress is; at the section of $\beta=0.3$ rad, the number of teeth does not affect the stress (σ=constant); and at the middle transverse section, the less the number of teeth is, the larger the stress is. This tendency is opposite to the one in Figure 7.2a-b.

Comparing two curves in Figures 7.2c and 7.2d, which have the same number of teeth, it is found that for a given transverse section (β), the stress magnitude $|\sigma|$ at the root fillet of the concave tooth is larger than on the convex tooth.

Generally, in Figure 7.2, the stress magnitude $|\sigma|$ decreases with the increase of the number of teeth. In the meantime, the stress almost does not change with the β when the number of teeth is 100. This is because when the number of teeth is increased, the load applied on the tooth is decreased.

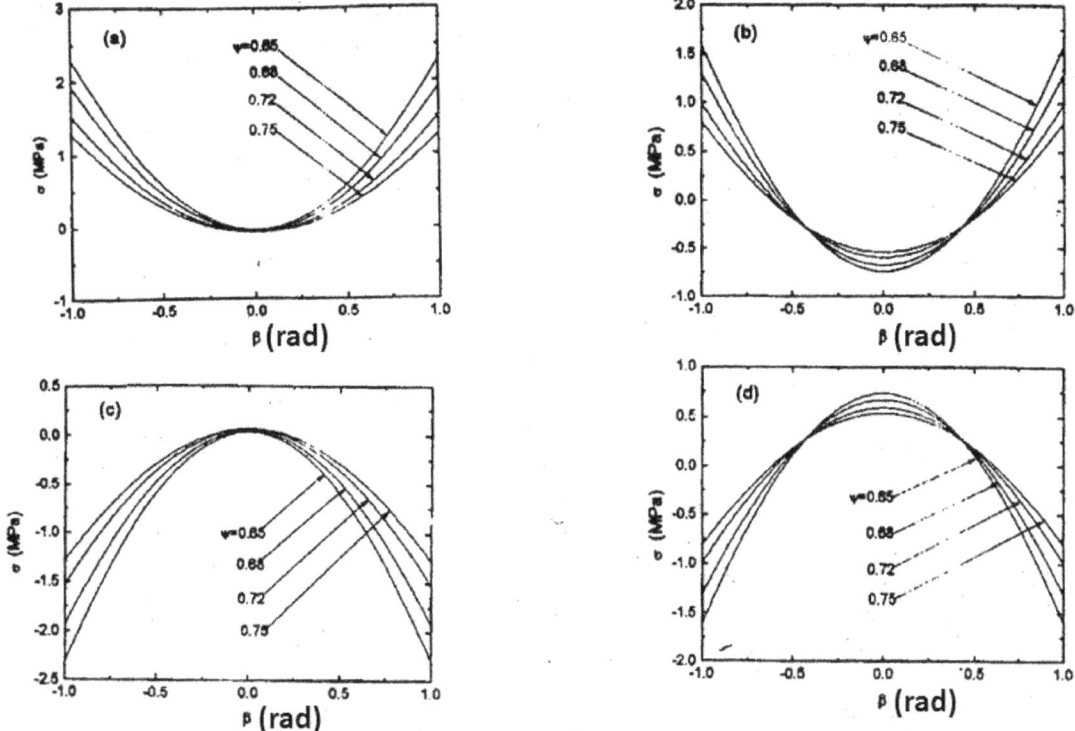

Figure 7.3 Stress and Helix Angle σ-β Histories for Four Given Tooth Width Factors at:

(a) the root fillet of convcave tooth with the load applied on the top of concave tooth

(b) the root fillet of convex tooth with the load applied on the top of concave tooth

(c) the root fillet of convcave tooth with the load applied on the top of convex tooth

(d) the root fillet of convex tooth with the load applied on the top of convex tooth

Also, in Figure 7.2, when the load is applied on the top of the concave tooth, the stress increases from the middle transverse section to two ends of tooth length. Conversely, when the load is applied on the top of the convex tooth, the stress decreases from the middle transverse section to the two ends of the tooth length.

Varying Tooth Width Factor: Figures 7.3a-d display the stress and helix angle σ-β histories for four given tooth width factors (see Appendix I): 0.65, 0.68, 0.72, and 0.75, when other parameters given in Table 7.1 are constant. In terms of the two sorts of loading conditions, the discussion is split into the following two groups.

Group I: As the load is applied on the top of the concave tooth, the stress distributions at the root fillets of the concave tooth and convex tooth are depicted in Figures 7.3a-b, respectively. For each curve, the stress distribution is symmetric to the middle transverse section, and the stress goes down from the two sides to the middle transverse section. The maximum stress presents at the two sides, and minimum stress presents in the middle transverse section.

For the four curves, at the two sides, the less the tooth width factor is, the higher the stress is; and at the middle transverse section, the smaller the tooth width factor is, the smaller the stress is.

Comparing two curves in Figure 7.3a and 7.3b, which have the same tooth width factor, it can be found that for a given transverse section, the stress at the root fillet of the concave tooth is larger than on the convex tooth.

Group II: As the load is applied on the top of the convex tooth, the stress distributions at the root fillets of the concave tooth and convex tooth are depicted in Figures 7.3c-d, respectively. For each curve, the stress distribution is symmetric to the middle transverse section, and the stress goes up from the two sides to the middle transverse section. The maximum stress presents in the middle transverse section, and minimum stress presents at two sides.

For the four curves, at the two sides, the less the tooth width factor is, the lower the stress is; and at the middle transverse section, the less the tooth width factor is, the higher the stress is. This tendency is opposite to the one in Figure 7.3a-b.

Comparing two curves in Figures 7.3c and 7.3d, which have the same tooth width factor, it can be seen that for a given transverse section (β), the stress magnitude $|\sigma|$ at the root fillet of the concave tooth is larger than on the convex tooth.

Generally, in Figure 7.3, it can conclude that the larger the tooth width factor is, the less the stress magnitude $|\sigma|$ is. The reason is that the larger the tooth width factor is, the longer the contact line, which results in lower distributed load.

Also, in Figure 7.3, the stress increases from the middle transverse section to two ends of tooth length when the load is applied on the top of the concave tooth. Conversely, when the load is applied on the top of the convex tooth, the stress decreases from the middle transverse section to the two ends of the tooth length.

The main conclusions obtained in this study are summarized as follows.
1. The bending stress distribution is symmetric to the middle transverse section.
2. The bending stress increases from the middle transverse section to two ends of tooth length when the load is applied on the top of the concave tooth. Conversely, when the load is applied on the top of the convex tooth, the bending stress decreases from the middle transverse section to the two ends of the tooth length.
3. The bending stress magnitude decreases with the increase of module, number of teeth, and tooth width factor.

8. Bending Strength of CATT Gear

The theoretical formula of the bending strength of a CATT gear is proposed by modifying the bending stress Equation 7.1 by adding more modified factors. The factor determinations and allowable bending stress determinations are addressed in detail.

Equation 7.1 in Chapter 7 is used as a basic formula to calculate the bending stress at tooth root fillet. In this Chapter, it is rewritten as Equation 8.1. Reviewing previous Chapters, basic assumptions are summarized as seven points:

1. The spatial contact line is simplified to a planar circular arc, and its length equals that of the arc of reference circular.
2. The tooth profile has a standard involute at any transverse section through the face width.
3. The full load is applied on the top of a single tooth in a static condition.
4. The radial and axial components are negligible.
5. The tangential component force is distributed uniformly along the full tooth trace.
6. The critical section can be determined according to the method of Hofer 30° tangential line.
7. The friction on the tooth face is neglected.
8. Stress concentration in the tooth root fillet is negligible.

$$\sigma = \frac{P_t}{Bm} Y_{Fa} \qquad (8.1)$$

The basic Equation 8.1 indicates that tooth bending stress varies with the tangential force P_t and form factor Y_{Fa} directly, but with the tooth width B and tooth module m inversely. Basic Equation 8.1 is not secured using for CATT gear strength analysts since it is established based on the above assumptions. The critical problems for Equation 8.1 are considered in the following seven points.

In first, the transverse tooth profile presents a standard involute only on the middle transverse section, and approximately involutes on any other transverse profile.

In the second, the tooth is loaded dynamically instead of being loaded statically. It is influenced by pitch line velocity.

In the third, the full load is shared by two teeth instead of the single tooth, because of CATT gear contact ratio is bigger than 1(Li, 1990).

In the fourth, the greatest load is not applied on the top of the tooth. When one pair of teeth contact happens, it is applied on much below the top of the tooth; while when two pairs of teeth contact happen, it is shared by two teeth.

In the fifth, the effect of the radial and axial component forces on the tooth fillet stress is ignored.

In the sixth, the effect of the stress concentration on the tooth root fillet is not considered. In fact, it will enlarge the stress at the fillet.

In the seventh, the tangential force is not distributed uniformly along the full tooth trace due to contact deformation.

If considering the influence of these factors on the bending stress σ_F, and taking account the allowable bending stress at the root $[\sigma]_F$, the bending strength is expressed as Equation 8.2.

$$\sigma_F = \frac{KP_t}{Bm} Y_{Fa} Y_{Sa} Y_\varepsilon Y_{ao} \leq [\sigma]_F \tag{8.2}$$

where K is the load factor, Y_{Fa} is the form factor, Y_{sa} is the stress concentration factor, Y_ε is the contact ratio factor, and Y_{ao} is the arc factor of the tooth CATT gear.

8.1 DETERMINATION OF FACTORS

1. Load factor K involves four factors and is given in Equation 8.3.

$$K = K_v K_A K_{Fa} K_{F\beta} \tag{8.3}$$

where K_v is the dynamic factor, which describes the severity of impact as successive pairs of teeth engage. It relates to the pitch line velocity v timing the number of teeth Z, as well as the manufacturing accuracy. Figure 8.1 (Qiu, and Xu, 1987) gives the dynamic factors with the manufacturing accuracy grades 3-10.

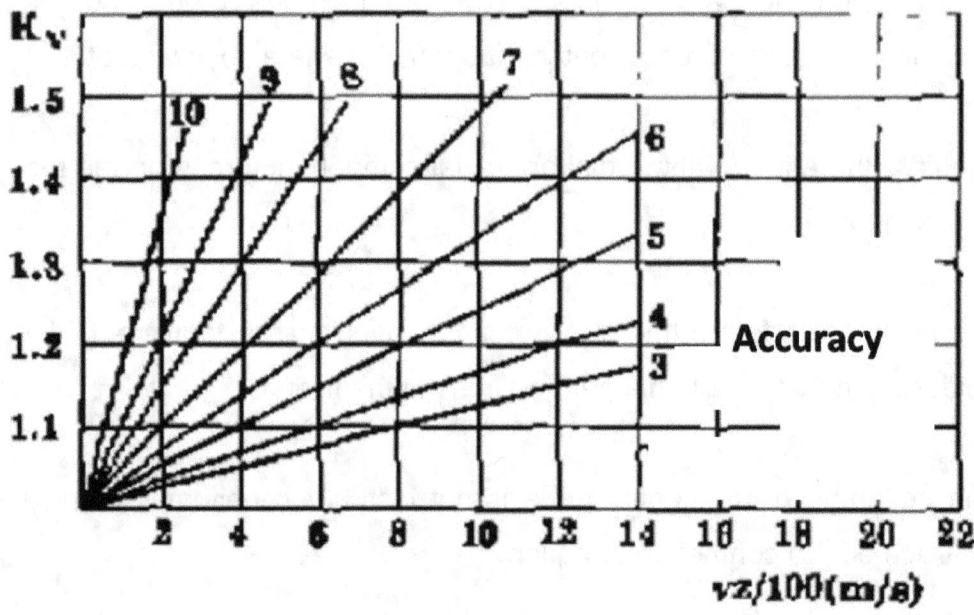

Figure 8.1 Dynamic Factor K_v

Figure 8.1 indicates that for a given accuracy grade, the dynamic factor increases with the increase of vZ; and for a given vZ, the dynamic factor increases with the increase of accuracy grade value.

K_A is the overload factor, which reflects the degree of non-uniformity of driving and load torques. It can be obtained by referring the overload factor of spur gear as given in Table 8.1 (Gopinath and Mayuram, 2013).

Table 8.1 Overload Factor K_A

	Driven Machinery		
Source of Power	Uniform	Moderate Shock	Heavy Shock
Uniform	1.00	1.25	1.75
Light Shock	1.25	1.50	2.00
Medium Shock	1.50	1.75	2.25

It notes that the overload factor ranges from 1 to 2.25. Specifically, 1 is assigned under the condition of the uniform operations of both driving machinery and driven machinery; and 2.25 is assigned under the condition of driving machinery with the medium shock and driven machinery with heavy shock.

$K_{F\alpha}$ is the transverse load distribution factor, which accounts for the effect of the non-uniform distribution of transverse load between several pairs of simultaneously contacting gear teeth. It depends on the accuracy grade of gears. Standard ISO (Standard ISO 6336-1, 2009) gives the transverse load distribution factor in Table 8.2.

Table 8.2 Transverse Load Distribution Factor $K_{F\alpha}$

Accuracy grade	6	7	8	9
Transverse Load Factor	1.0	1.1	1.2	1.3

It notes that the transverse load factor increases from 1 to 1.3 with the increase of accuracy grade from 6 to 9.

$K_{F\beta}$ is the longitudinal load distribution factor, which accounts for the non-uniform spread of the load across the face width. It depends on the accuracy of mounting, bearings, shaft deflection, and accuracy of gears. CATT gear longitudinal load distribution factor is given in Equation 8.4 by adding a deformation factor ξ to the longitudinal load distribution factor of spur gear K_β.

$$Y_{F\beta} = \xi Y_\beta \tag{8.4}$$

Contact deformation makes the tangential force distribution present non-uniformly along the full tooth trace (Zheng, 1989). ξ is defined as the ratio of the bending stress at the tooth root fillet caused by the maximum load intensity to the bending stress at the fillet caused by the average load, which is uniformly distributed on the contact lines at the worst position. The result is expressed as Equation 8.4a (Li and Shi, 1992).

$$\xi = \frac{\cos\beta \sin\frac{\beta_0}{2}}{\frac{\beta_0}{2} + \frac{\sin\beta_0}{2}} X \tag{8.4a}$$

where β is the helix angle, β_0 is the central angle and

$$X = \sqrt{\frac{\left(\frac{-h_F y}{I'_{x0x0}} - \frac{\tan\alpha_n}{S_F}\right)^2 + \left(\frac{2.5}{S_F}\right)^2}{\left(\frac{-h_F y B}{I_{x0x0}} - \frac{\tan\alpha_n}{\beta_0 S_F}\ln\frac{1+\varphi}{1-\varphi}\right)^2 + \left(\frac{2.5}{S_F}\right)^2}} \tag{8.4a-a}$$

where h_F is the distance between the critical section and the most unfavorable point (see Equation 3.1), S_F is the width of the critical section (see Equation 3.2) and α_n is the pressure angle, φ is the tooth width factor (see Appendix I), and

$$y = y_0 - R\left(\cos\frac{\beta_0}{2} - \cos\beta\right) \qquad (8.4\text{a-b})$$

where R is the radius of reference circular, and y_0 is the vertical distance from the centroid of critical section to the axis X (see Figure 4.1) and is given in Equation 4.7.

Let b denote the unit tooth width, then

$$I'_{x0x0} = \frac{bS_F^3}{12} + bS_F\left(-y + \frac{S_F}{2}\right)^2 \qquad (8.4\text{a-c})$$

Instituting Equations 8.4a and 8.4a-a–8.4a-c to Equation 8.4, it can find the longitudinal load distribution factor $K_{F\beta}$ is the function of the helix angle β. Thus, $K_{F\beta}$ varies along with the tooth trace.

Longitudinal load distribution factor of spur gear K_β is given in Table 8.3 (Gopinath and Mayuram, 2013).

Table 8.3 Longitudinal Load Distribution Factor of Spur Gear K_β

Characteristics of Support	Face Width (mm)			
	0-50	150	225	>400
Accurate mountings, small bearing clearances, minimum deflection, precision gears	1.3	1.4	1.5	1.8
Less rigid mountings, less accurate gears, contact across the full face	1.6	1.7	1.8	2.2
Accuracy and mounting such that less than full-face contact exists	>2.2	>2.2	>2.2	>2.2

2. The form factor Y_{Fa} describes the tooth shape and geometric property. It depends mainly on the tooth width B, module m, distance h_F (between the

critical section and the most unfavorable point), and the moment of inertia of critical section about its horizontal neutral axis I_{x0x0}. It can be calculated using Equation 8.5, which is derived in Equation 7.1a in Chapter 7.

$$Y_{Fa} = \frac{-Bmh_F y}{I_{x0x0}} \tag{8.5}$$

Note that Y_{Fa} is the function of y. Hence, there is different Y_{Fa} at each transverse section.

3. The stress concentration factor Y_{sa} takes into account the enlarged stress at the critical section due to the fillet at the tooth root. The tooth profile of a CATT gear is assumed to have a standard involute at any transverse section through the face width. The method establishing the stress concentration factor equation of spur gear is employed to the CATT gear. It is expressed as Equation 8.6 (Standard ISO 6336-3, 1996).

$$Y_{sa} = \left(1.2 + 0.16\frac{S_F}{h_F}\right)\left(\frac{S_F}{2\rho_F}\right)^{\left(\frac{1}{1.2+2.1\frac{h_F}{S_F}}\right)} \tag{8.6}$$

where ρ_F is the fillet radius at the critical section (see Equation 3.3).

Since h_F, S_F and ρ_F are the function of helix angle β, they change from the middle transverse section to the two ends' transverse sections as indicated in Chapter 3. Thus, Y_{sa} has a different value at each transverse section, which is positioned by β.

4. The contact ratio factor Y_ε reflects the effect of the transverse contact ratio ε on the bending stress. It depends on the tooth geometric parameters and engaging situation. It is given as Equation 8.7 (Chen, 1988), which is the contact ratio of spur gear plus additional contact ratio.

$$\varepsilon = \frac{1}{2\pi}(Z_1(\tan \alpha_{a1} - \tan \alpha') + Z_2(\tan \alpha_{a2} - \tan \alpha'))$$
$$+ \frac{R}{\pi m}\left(1 - \sqrt{1 - \varphi^2}\right) \tag{8.7}$$

where Z_1 is the number of teeth on the driving gear, Z_2 is the number of teeth on the driven gear, α_{a1} is the pressure angle of addendum circle on driving gear, α_{a2} is the pressure angle of addendum circle on driven gear, α' is the working pressure angle, R is the radius of reference circular, and φ is the tooth width factor.

Then

$$Y_\varepsilon = 0.2 + \frac{0.8}{\varepsilon} \tag{8.8}$$

In Equation 8.7, it is known that the CATT contact ratio consists of two components: the contact ratio of spur gear (the first item) plus the additional contact ratio (the last item). Therefore, the CATT contact ratio factor is less than the spur gear one in the result of decreasing the bending stress.

5. The arc factor Y_{ao} considers the effect of the arc tooth structure and arc tooth trace on the bending stress. Since the radial and axial components are negligible, the bending stress Equation 8.2 does not include the bending stress components σ_3 and σ_4 caused by the radial and axial forces, respectively (see Equations 5.5 and 5.7 in Chapter 5). Thus, Y_{ao} is added to Equation 8.2 to modify the bending stress calculation.

Y_{ao} depends on the module m divided by the reference circular radius R and the tooth width factor φ. In Appendix I, it suggests the tooth width factor φ=0.65-0.75. As the purpose of the study, Luo (Luo, 1987) gives the arc factor Y_{ao} responding to the tooth width factors between 0.60 and 0.70 with an interval of 0.02 as shown in Figure 8.2.

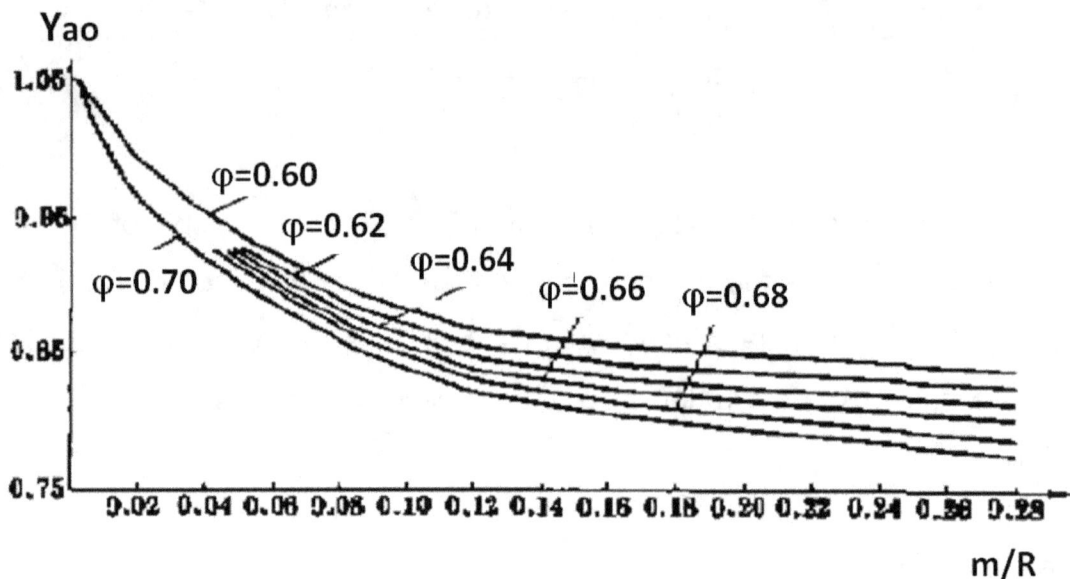

Figure 8.2 Arc Factor Y_{ao} (Luo, 1987)

In Figure 8.2, it notes that for a given tooth width factor φ, the arc factor Y_{ao} decreases with the increase of m/R; while for a given m/R, the arc factor Y_{ao} decreases with the increase of the tooth width factor φ. It indicates that the bigger the tooth width factor is, the more curvertual the tooth is, and in the result that the smaller the arc factor is. In the design of CATT gear, the arc factor is expected to be smaller than 1 in order to decrease the bending stress.

8.2 DETERMINATION OF ALLOWABLE BENDING STRESS

The bending strength Equation 8.2 requires the calculated bending stress at the tooth root fillet is not to exceed the allowable bending stress at the same position. The allowable bending stress at the tooth root fillet $[\sigma]_F$ can be calculated from Equation 8.9 (Standard GB3480-83, 1983).

$$[\sigma]_F = \frac{\sigma_{0F}}{S_{0F}} Y_N Y_X \qquad (8.9)$$

where σ_{0F} is the material endurance limit of the bending stress as gear tooth is subjected to one-way bending. It can be obtained from Table 8.3 (Qiu, and Xu, 1987).

Table 8.3 Endurance Limit of Bending Stress for Unidirectional Loading

Material	Heat Treatment	Surface Hardness	Core Hardness	σ_{0F} (Mpa)
Carbon Steel and Alloy Steel	Normalized or Conditioned	HB180-350	HB180-350	1.8HB
Alloy Steel	Integral Quenched	HRC45-55	HRC45-55	500
Alloy Steel	Surface Quenched	HRC48-58	HRC27-35	600
Alloy Steel	Nitrided	HV350-750	HRC25-40	12HRC+300
Alloy Steel steel	Carburized and Quenched	HRC57-62	HRC30-45	750

S_{0F} is the factor of safety for bending failure. Usually, it is set to 1.75-2.2. The highest value of 2.2 is assigned for the gears, which require high reliability or are made of cast steel or works in the high temperature or corrosion environment.

Y_x is the size factor. It relates to the module of gear m and can be chosen from Table 8.4.

Table 8.4 Size Factor Y_x

m	3	5	10	20
Y_x	1	0.96	0.91	0.87

Y_N is the stress cycle factor for bending strength. Let mm denotes the crack growth rate constant, and N denotes the number of cycles or the equivalent number of cycles, Y_N can be given by Equation 8.9.

$$Y_N = \sqrt[mm]{\frac{4 \times 10^6}{N}} \qquad (8.9)$$

There are two cases of fatigue loading, such as the constant amplitude with proportional loading and the constant amplitude with non-proportional loading.

For constant amplitude with proportional loading, N is given as Equation 8.9a.

$$N = 60nt_h \tag{8.9a}$$

where n is the gear revolution speed, and t_h is the operation time.

For constant amplitude with non-proportional loading, if there are k loading levels, the equivalent number of cycles N is given as Equation 8.9b (Qiu, and Xu, 1987).

$$N = 60 \sum_{i=1}^{k} n_i \, t_{hi} \left(\frac{T_i}{T_{max}}\right)^{mm} \tag{8.9b}$$

where the ith level has the gear revolution speed n_i, the operation time t_{hi}, and torque T_i. T_{max} is the maximum torque overall levels.

In Equations 8.9a and 8.9b, if N equal or larger than 1, then Y_N=1.

In Equations 8.9 and 8.9b, for the normalized or conditioned gear, mm=6; and for the integral quenched or surface quenched, or nitrided gear, mm=9.

REFERENCES

1. Gopinath, K. and Mayuram, M.M.M. 2013. Machine Design II. Indian Institute of Technology Madras. New Delhi.
2. Li, Y. and Zhao, X.Y. 1993. Calculation of Bending Stress of CATT Gear. Journal of New Technology and New Process, No.5, pp.14-15.

3. Li, Y. 1990. Bending Strength Analysis of CATT Cylindrical Gear. M.S. Thesis, North China Institute of Technology, Taiyuan, China.
4. Standard ISO 6336-1, 2009. Calculation of load capacity of spur and helical gears - Part 1: Basic principles, introduction and general influence factors.
5. Standard ISO 6336-3, 1996. Calculation of Load Capacity of Spur and Helical Gears - Part 3: Calculation of Tooth Bending Strengh, First edition.
6. Li, Y. and Shi, Y.H. 1992. The Effect of Contact Deformation of Line Contact Circular-Arc-Tooth-Trace Gear. Journal of North China Institute of Technology, Vol.13 No.1, pp.54-57.
7. Standard GB3480-83. 1983. Calculation of Load Capacity for Involute Cylindrical Gear Teeth.
8. Qiu, X.H and Xu, Z.Y.1987. Machine Elements. Mechanical Manufacturing Publisher, Beijing, China.
9. Chen, J.1988. Tooth Surface Forming Principle and Engaging Characteristics of a Circular-Arc Tooth-Trace Cylindrical Gear. Master Degree Thesis, North China Institute of Technology.
10. Zheng, J. 1989. Contact Strength Analysis of a Circular-Arc-Tooth-Trace Cylindrical Gear. M.S. Thesis, North China Institute of Technology.

9. Experimental Test of Bending Stress Distributions along the Tooth Trace at Tooth Root Fillet

The experimental test is carried out for validating theoretical calculation of bending stress distributions along the tooth trace at the tooth root fillet for a CATT gear. The theoretical formula has been finalized as Equation 8.2 by adding a series of factors into simple stress Equation 8.1. In this Chapter, the strain gauge method is proposed to test the strain at the root fillet. The strain Equation is derived from Hooke's law and Equation 8.2. The validation is performed by comparing and analyzing the theoretical results and experimental results.

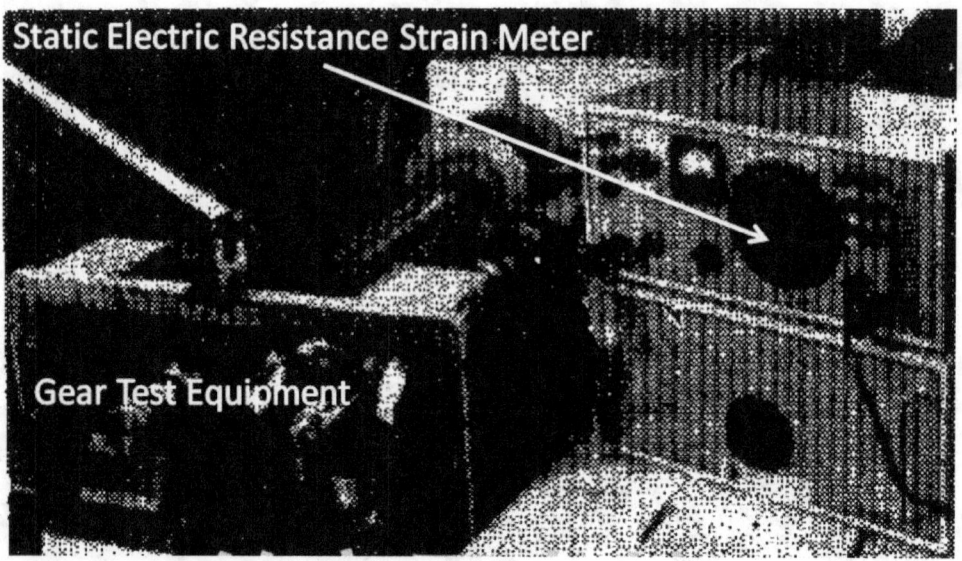

Figure 9.1 Experiment Equipment and Setup

9.1 EXPERIMENT SETUP

Figure 9.1 shows the experiment equipment and setup. The experimental procedure is performed on a modified gear test equipment of model ZHD-82A for the loading application and a static electric resistance strain meter of model YTD-5 for the strain acquisition. The pictures were taken at our lab in 1988, when I worked on my master's degree project. Thus, it looks blurry but still can see the profiles of the equipment and meter, as well as their layout.

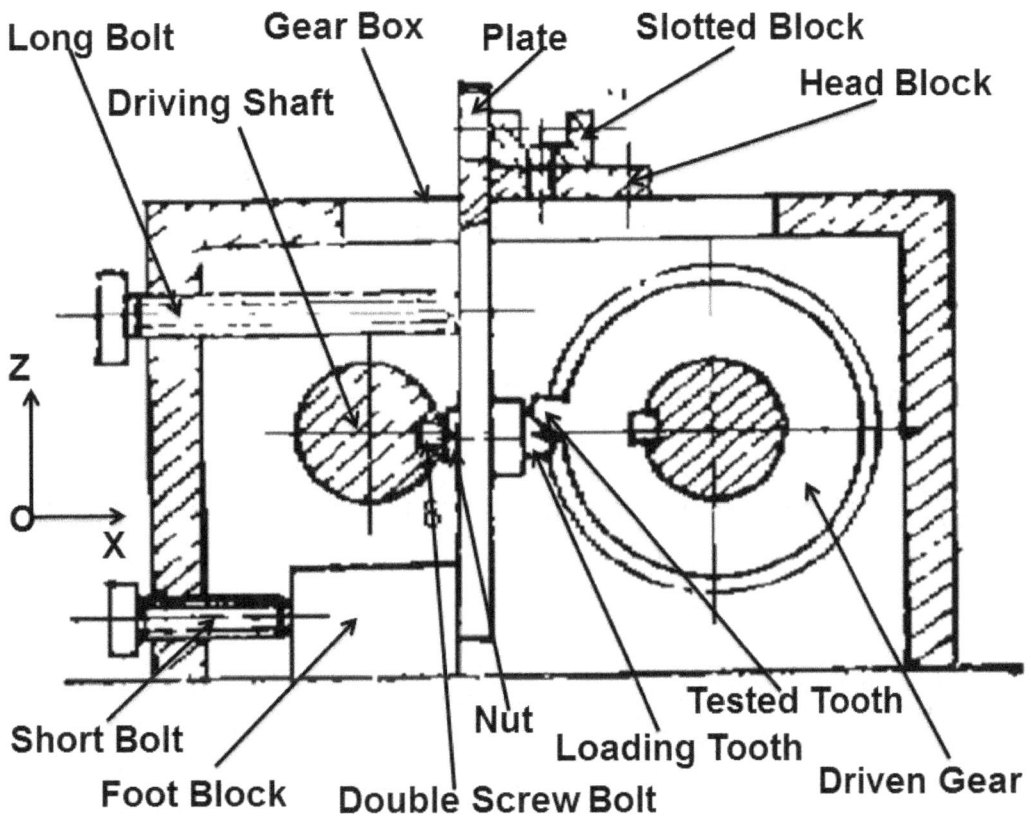

Figure 9.2 A Front View Schematic Diagram of Experiment Device and Equipment

Figure 9.2 shows a front view schematic diagram of a static loading device installed on the gear test equipment. A global coordinate system $O(X, Y, Z)$ is attached to the equipment on the ground. The typical units consist of a gearbox, a loading tooth, a driven gear, a tested tooth, two adjusting assemblies, and three supporting assemblies. The design features of the loading device are indicated below in detail, and the structures of components and connections are described.

The critical consideration in the loading device design is to ensure that a pair of teeth is precisely engaged in and loaded during tests. For statically simulating reality, a pair of engaged teeth is developed, designed, and manufactured. Two tasks are involved.

First of all, a driven gear (tested gear) is installed in the gear test equipment, and the neighboring teeth are cut off in order to eliminate the influence of other engaged teeth on the tested tooth. This consideration is just to match the assumption of a pair of teeth engaged as building Equation 8.2.

Second of all, the driving gear is removed from the equipment. One of the cut teeth from the driven gear is utilized as the engaged tooth named as loading tooth. The two works are focused on: one, positioning the driving tooth for engagement and two, enhancing the strength and stiffness of connecting components for accurate engagement.

1. Driving Tooth Position

For positioning purposes, the loading device allows the loading tooth to be able to translate in X independently, Y and Z directions as well as rotate in the X-direction.

X-Y-Z translations are performed in an adjusting assembly, which consists of the loading tooth, plate, slotted block, and head block (fixed with the gearbox). Since the loading tooth is joined to the plate, the job downgrades to adjust the position of the plate in X-Y-Z directions. The plate is connected to the slotted block, which is coupled with a X-Y sliding plane on the head block. This arrangement permits moving the slotted block on the surface of the head block along the X or Y axis to position the loading tooth. Also, the plate is coupled with a sliding left surface of the slotted block in the Z-direction. This design permits vertically moving the plate to adjust the loading tooth in the Z-direction. Once making sure that every adjustment is made, all bolts & nuts, which joined the plate to the slotted block and the slotted block to the head block, are tightened.

X revolution is adjustable automatically in another adjusting assembly, which consists of the loading tooth, plate, long bolt and nut, and driving shaft (fixed with the gearbox). Since the loading tooth is screwed to the double screw bolt, the job downgrades to adjust the revolution of the double screw bolt in the X-direction. It notes that the loading tooth is joined to the plate by the double screw bolt and nut, and then the double screw bolt goes through the plate and is fixed on the driving shaft. Once the driving tooth is engaged in the tested tooth, the contact characteristic of the circular arc tooth trace allows automatically rotating the driving tooth in direction X until the pair of teeth is centrally aligned.

2. Components Strength and Stiffness

The plate is a vital part of this device. Enhancements of its strength and stiffness are important considerations to ensure the meshing preciousness of the pair of teeth. Initially, it is a simple plate and mounted on the slotted block at the head. For significantly reducing the deformation of the plate, additional three supports are set in X directions.

X-direction deformation of the plate is limited by the nut, which is locked together in a supporting assembly consisting of the plate, double screw bolt, nut, and driving shaft (fixed with the gearbox). The nut screwing with the double screw bolt presses the left surface of the plate in the X-direction. In fact, this assembly functions as both positioning the driving tooth and supporting the plate.

X-direction deformation of the plate is resisted by the long bolt, which is included in a simply supporting assembly consisting of the plate, long bolt, and gearbox. The long bolt screwed with the gearbox directly touches the left surface of the plate to form a push configuration in the X-direction.

X-direction deformation of the plate is restrained by the foot block, which is arranged in a supporting assembly consisting of the plate, foot block, short bolt, and gearbox. The short bolt screwed with the gearbox touches the left surface of the foot block, and then the foot block touches the left surface of the plate. This arrangement constructs a push-push configuration in the X-direction. Comparing this assembly with the above one, it includes a foot block between the short bolt and the plate. The foot block increases the contact area with the plate.

9.2 MODEL LOADING AND STRAIN ACQUISITION

1. Model Loading

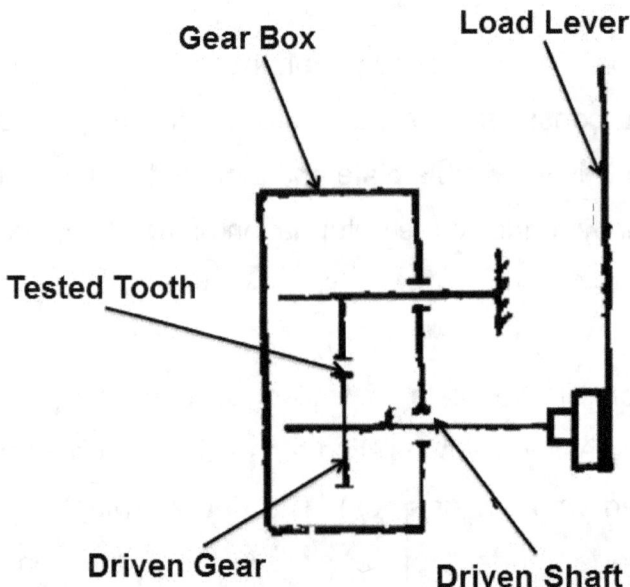

Figure 9.3 Schematic Diagram of Lever Static Load

Figure 9.3 shows the static torque is applied to the tested gear through a lever plus weights and a thin-long driven shaft. The weight is changeable according to the required torque. Result torque is calculated by the weight multiplying the distance between the point of the weight application and the central axis of the driven shaft. This torque is equal to the torque applied to the driving tooth. Adjusting the position of the driving tooth and let the torque applied on the top of the tested tooth to match the assumption of the load applied on the top of the calculated tooth in Equation 8.2.

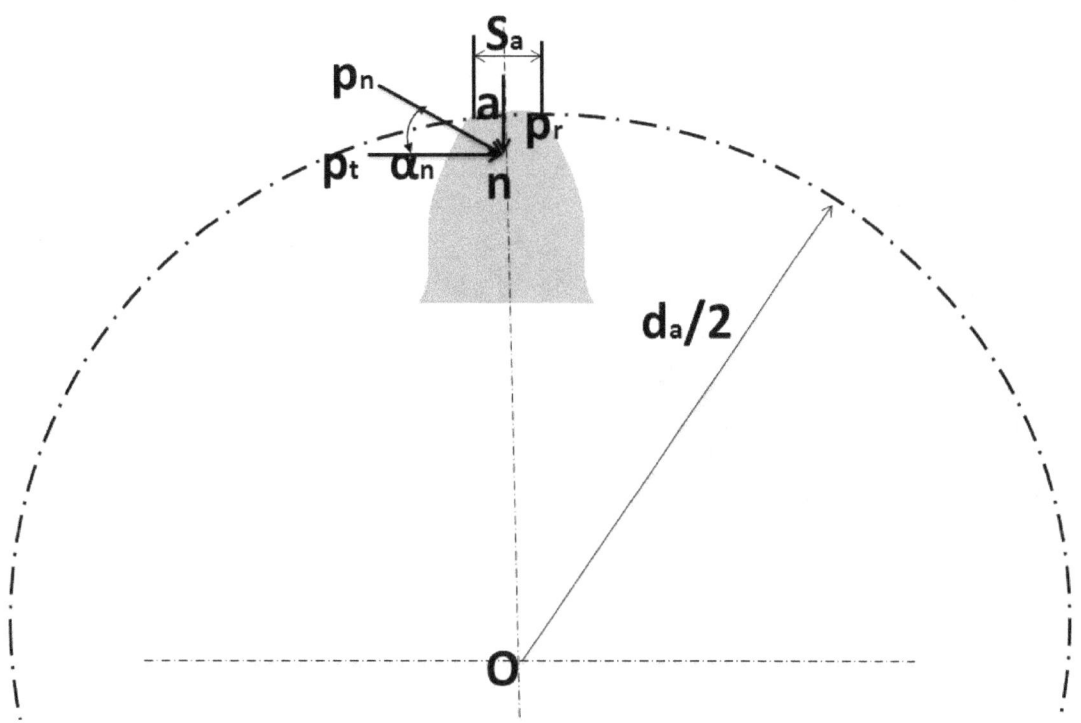

Figure 9.4 Total Tooth Forces Acted on Tooth Top of CATT Gear

In Equation 8.2, the force component associated with the torque is only the tangential component force P_t. This point has been indicated in Chapter 2. As shown in Figure 9.4 (from Figure 2.3a), P_t is applied on the tooth top point n, which is the intersection of normal component force and central line of addendum circle at the middle transverse section. Resolved P_t has been written as Equation 2.1. Here, it is given as Equation 9.1 for illustration purposes.

$$P_t = \frac{T}{oa - na} = \frac{2T}{d_a - S_a \tan \alpha_n} \quad (9.1)$$

where T is the torque generated on the driven gear, d_a is the diameter of addendum circle, S_a is the tooth thickness at addendum circle, and α_n is the pressure angle at addendum circle.

2. Strain Acquisition

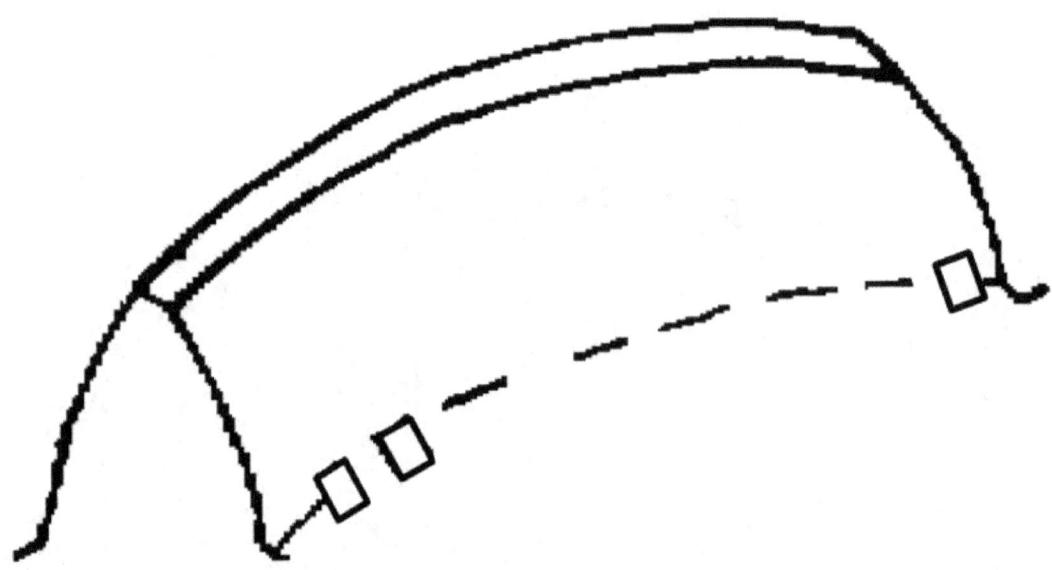

Figure 9.5 Tested Tooth with Arrangement of Strain Gauges

Theoretically, the critical section is determined according to the method of Hofer 30° tangential line; while experimentally, the strain gauges are approximately attached in the root fillet of the tested tooth. Figure 9.5 shows that electric resistance strain gauges of square 1x1 mm² are adhered to the tested tooth along the tooth trace on the root fillet of the concave tooth and are arranged in a line. The difference between the two neighboring strain gauges is 5 mm. The same works have been done for the convex tooth.

Using signal wires, all strain gauges are connected with the YTD-5 static electric resistance strainmeter. The signal collection can be summarized as five steps: a) the strain gauges measure strains; b) signal wires transfer the data to the strainmeter; c) the strainmeter stores the data; d) the screen shows the data; and e) the data are recorded.

9.3. CASE STUDY AND BENDING STRENGTH FORMULA VALIDATION

1. Bending Strain Equation

Figure 9.6 shows a schematic diagram of a critical section for evaluating strain at root fillet for the tested tooth of CATT gear. The symbols used in this section are indicated there. A local Cartesian coordinate o(x, y) is attached to the critical section with the origin o on the centroid C_0. Horizontal axis x coincides with the horizontal neutral axis x_0x_0; and the vertical axis y coincides with the vertical neutral axis y_0y_0.

As illustrated in Chapter 2, y_0 is the vertical distance from its centroid C_0 to the line AG of the critical section. Also, the reference-circular radius of convex tooth R_1 is assumed to equal to one of concave tooth R_2, which is $R_1=R_2=R$. B represents the tooth width, and m donates the tested gear module in the middle transverse section. Central angle β_0 is marked in Figure 9.6 too.

The strain is calculated using the theory of elasticity, Hooke's law. That is the strain of the tested tooth is proportional to the stress applied to it. If E represents the elastic modulus of tooth material, then strain ε = bending stress σ_F divided by E. Nothing the bending stress Equation 8.2, the general strain at the root fillet of the tested tooth can be conducted by Equation 9.2.

$$\varepsilon = \frac{KP_t}{EBm} Y_{Fa} Y_{Sa} Y_{\varepsilon} Y_{ao} \tag{9.2}$$

As discussed in Chapter 8, for a given gear, where K is the load factor and the function of helix angle β; Y_{Fa} is the form factor and the function of y; Y_{sa} is the stress concentration factor and the function of helix angle β; Y_ε is the contact ratio factor and a constant; and Y_{ao} is the arc factor of the tooth CATT gear and a constant.

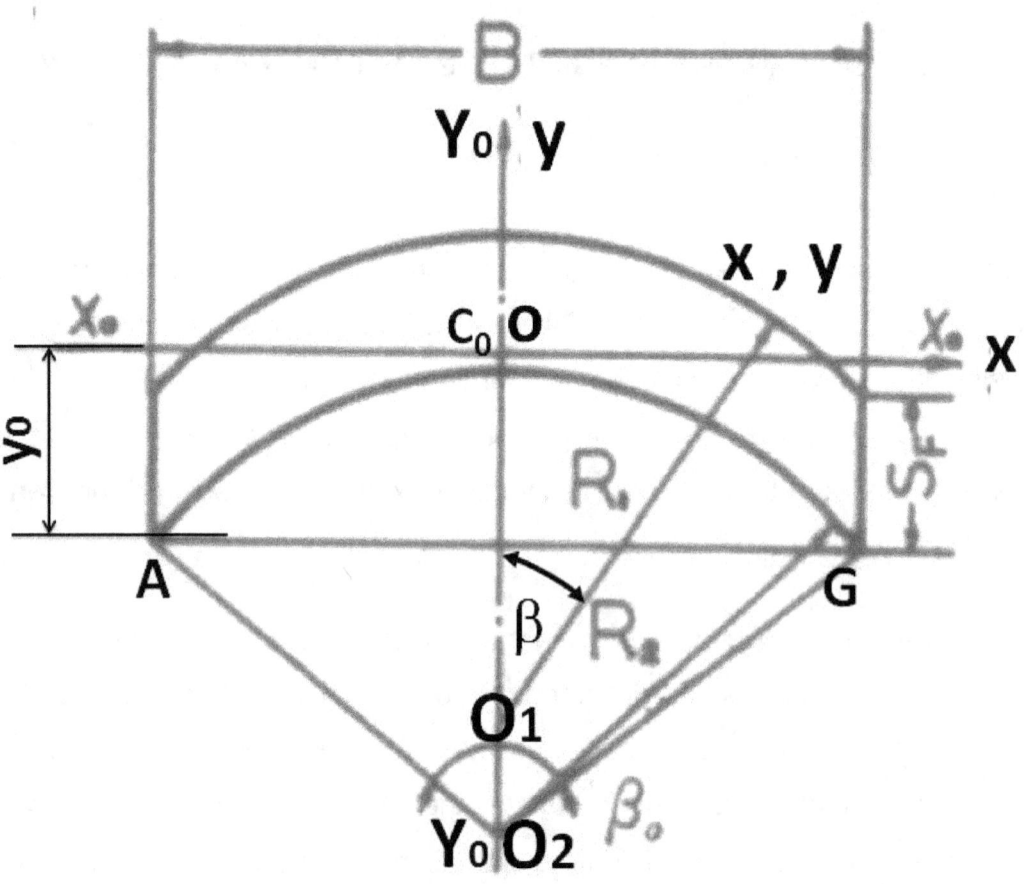

Figure 9.6 A Schematic Diagram of Critical Section for Tested Tooth of A CATT Gear

In Figure 9.6, at a selected point x, y, the geometric relationship between vertical position y and helix angle β is given as Equation 9.3; and the geometric relationship between horizontal position x and helix angle β is indicated in Equation 9.4.

$$y = -y_0 + R\left(\cos\beta - \cos\frac{\beta_0}{2}\right) \tag{9.3}$$

$$\beta = \sin^{-1}\frac{x}{R} \tag{9.4}$$

Likely mentioned above, K, Y_{Fa} and Y_{sa} are functions of position y or helix angle β. In Equations 9.3-9.4, it notes that both y and β relate to position x. Hence, ε is a function of x. Furthermore, since ε is proportional to σ_F, the higher σ_F, the larger the ε.

2. Results and Discussion

The bending strains at the root fillets of the concave tooth and convex tooth are measured, respectively. Table 9.1 lists the basic parameters of a pair of meshing gears in the middle transverse section (Li, 1990; Li and Zhao, 1992 and 1997). The material used for the two gears is steel $45^{\#}$. The mechanics properties of gears, such as the high tensile strength, high yield strength and high hardness, are obtained by quenching and tempering heat treatment. The accuracy degree grade of both gears is 8.

Table 9.1 Basic Parameters of a Pair of Meshing Gears at Middle Transverse Section

Number of Teeth		Module (mm)	Pressure Angle (degree)	Tooth Width (mm)		Cutter Radius (mm)		Degree of Accuracy
Z_1	Z_2	m	α	B_1	B_2	Inside Edge	Outside Edge	
62	62	3.226	20	44	44	116.52	116.52	8

Two gears have same size and parameters. The number of the driving gear teeth Z_1 is equal to the number of the driven gear teeth Z_2. The tooth width of the driving gear B_1 is equal to the tooth width of the driven gear tooth B_2. There are the same sizes of reference-circular radius for both the driving gear and the driven gear. The cutter radius of the inside edge or outside edge equals to the reference-circular radius of convex or concave, where R_1 or R_2. Module m and pitch pressure angles α for both gears are measured in the middle transverse section.

The two groups of tensile strains are measured by reading the strain gauges with two loading cases, respectively. One is when the load is applied on the top of the concave tooth, the strains are measured along the root fillet of the concave tooth. Another one is when the load is applied on the top of the convex tooth, the strains are measured along the root fillet of the convex tooth.

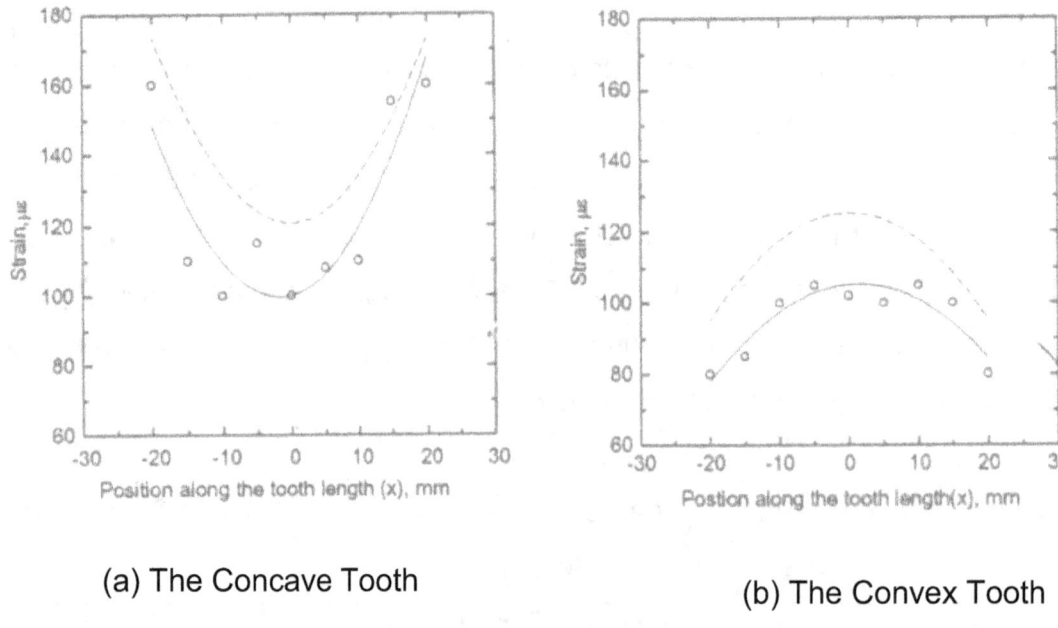

(a) The Concave Tooth   (b) The Convex Tooth

Figure 9.7 Strain Distributions along the Tooth Length at the Root Fillet

Figure 9.7 shows the strain(ε)-position(x) histories along the tooth length at the root fillet as the loading torque of 120 Nm applied on the top of the concave tooth and convex tooth, respectively. Respective strain distributions on the concave tooth and convex tooth are plotted based on the experimental results (solid lines) and the theoretical results (dash lines). According to two kinds of loading conditions, the results are discussed in two cases.

Case I: As the load is applied on the top of the concave tooth, the tensile strain distributions at the root fillets of the concave tooth are presented in Figure 9.7a. The strain curves from both the theoretical calculation and experimental measurement exhibit u-parabolic shapes. For the theoretical curve, the strain distribution is symmetric to the middle transverse section and the strain decreases from the two sides to the middle transverse section. The maximum strain of 175 µε occurs at the two sides and a minimum one of 120 µε occurs in the middle transverse section. For the experimental curve, the strain distribution is approximately symmetric to the middle transverse section, and the strain decreases from the two sides to the middle transverse section. Approximately, the maximum strain of 160 µε occurs at the two sides and a minimum one of 100 µε occurs in the middle transverse section.

Consequently, the tensile bending stress increases gradually from the middle transverse section to the two ends of the tooth length. In the meantime, the compressive stress at the convex tooth fillet is established. So, the critical transverse section is located at the two ends of the tooth length.

It notes that for a given position x, tensile strain is larger from the theoretical calculation than from the experimental measurement. This result certificates the stress and strain Equations 8.2 and 9.2 are secured to evaluate the bending strength of a CATT gear.

Case II: As the load is applied on the top of the convex tooth, the tensile strain distributions at the root fillets of the convex tooth are presented in Figure 9.7b. The strain curves for both the theoretical calculation and the experimental measurement exhibit n-parabolic shapes. For the theoretical curve, the strain distribution is symmetric to the middle transverse section and the strain increases from the two sides to the middle transverse section. The maximum strain of 130 µε occurs at the middle transverse section; while minimum one of 90 µε occurs in the two ends of the tooth. For the experimental curve, the strain distribution is approximately symmetric to the middle transverse section, and the strain increases from the two sides to the middle transverse section. Approximately, the maximum strain of 105 µε occurs at the middle transverse section; while minimum one of 80 µε occurs in the two ends.

Therefore, the tensile bending stress decreases gradually from the middle transverse section to the two ends of the tooth length. In this case, the concave tooth root fillet bears the compressive stress. Thus, the critical transverse section is located in the middle transverse section.

It notes that for a given position x, the strain is larger from the theoretical calculation than from the experimental measurement. Again, this result verifies that the stress and strain Equations 8.2 and 9.2 are reliable to evaluate the bending strength of a CATT gear.

Comparing the results of two cases, the tensile strain at the root fillet of the concave tooth is bigger than at the convex tooth. Clearly, the critical transverse section is not always located in the middle transverse section. The results of both theoretical calculation and experimental measurements support that the position of the critical transverse section depends on the side of the tooth surface when the load is applied.

In both cases, the predicted values are in agreement with the experimental ones. The predicted values are significantly larger than the experimental ones. A series of predictions and experiments are also done in the torques ranging from 50 to 120 Nm. All predicted and experimental results show similar trends, and the errors between the theoretical predictions and the experimental results are less than 25%.

The conclusion of theoretical predictions being greater than the experimental results validates the potential of the theoretical Equation 8.2 to predict the bending strength of CATT gear tooth. The analysis results identify that this equation will give higher safety confidence in the determination of the critical transverse section. The analysis results also illustrate that the theoretical calculation and experimental measurement can capture the stress distributions at the root fillet along the tooth length under the gear loading conditions.

REFERENCES

1. Li, Y. 1990. Test and Analysis on Bending Stress of Line Contact CATT Gear. Master Degree Student Thesis, North University of China, China.
2. Li, Y. and Zhao, XY. 1997. Distributions of Bending Stress along the Length of Tooth in the CATT Cylindrical Gear Tooth at the Tooth Fillet. The International Conference on Mechanical Transmissions and Mechanisms, July 1-4, 1997, Tianjin, P. R. China, pp.649-652.
3. Li, Y. and Zhao, X.Y. 1992. Experimental Study on Bending Stress of Line Contact Circular-arc-tooth-trace Gear. Journal of Aviation, Metrology and Measurement, No.3, pp.14-16.
4. Budynas, R.G. and Nisbett, J.K.. 2011. Shigley's Mechanical Engineering Design, 9th Ed.. The McGraw Hill Companies, New York.

10. Error Analysis and Corrections

In engineering design and analysis, the CATT gear bending strength formula still takes a dominant role, even though the modern advanced technology of the finite element analysis method can get more accurate results. The traditional formula evaluates the design fast, immediately, and in time. It is acceptable by the most engineers who may only hold bachelor degrees or even graduate degrees. Therefore, making the formula more accurate always is paid attention and effort by researchers and engineers.

In Chapter 8-9, either the theoretical predictions or the experimental measurements are all based on some simplifications and assumptions, which do not avoid producing the theoretical errors and experimental errors. In this chapter, these two kinds of errors are analyzed by addressing the simplifications and assumptions in Chapters 2, 5, 8 and 9.

10.1 THEORETICAL ERROR ANALYSIS

The theoretical errors are caused by the following aspects:
1) Basic bending stress Equation is established based on the assumption that the gear tooth is a cantilever beam in Chapter 5. The classic formula, $\sigma=-My/I$, (Gere and Timoshenko, 1997) for bending stress is used. Accuracy cannot be secured, and the result at best is only approximate because the tooth is short and thick and non-uniform in the critical section. It must be remembered that the

derivation of the equation for bending stress is assumed along a thin beam of a constant cross-section.

2) Tangential force P_t in the bending stress Equation is calculated by simplifying the spatial contact line to a planar arc, and its length equals that of the reference-circular arc in Chapter 2. Actually, while a pair of CATT gears engages in contact, the initial contact is a point, and then the contact changes into a line. As the teeth come into more engagement, the contact extends all the way across the tooth face with a series of complex spatial curves. The final contact becomes a point again.

And also, assume that the tangential component force is distributed uniformly along the full tooth trace. In fact, the tangential force is not distributed uniformly along the full tooth trace due to contact deformation.

3) The tooth profile is assumed to have a standard involute at any transverse section through the face width in Chapter 2. In fact, the transverse tooth profile presents a standard involute only on the middle transverse section and approximately involutes on any other transverse profile.

4) The radial and axial component forces are negligible in Chapter 8. When a pair of CATT gears goes into engagement, the radial force will cause the bending stress and compressive stress on the critical section. Also, the axial force will lead the bending stress on the critical section. The details are addressed in Chapter 5.

5) The friction on the tooth face is neglected in Chapter 8. In fact, when a pair of CATT gears engages in contact, the friction will produce between two surfaces of teeth.

6) The stress concentration on the tooth root fillet is not considered in the basic bending stress Equation 8.1. In fact, it will enlarge the stress at the fillet.

In order to correct the above errors, five modified factors are added to bending stress Equation 8.1, and final Equation is written as Equation 8.2. They are the load factor K, form factor Y_{Fa}, stress concentration factor Y_{sa}, contact ratio factor Y_ε and arc factor Y_{ao}. Load factor K involves four factors. The first three (see Section 8.1) heritage from spur gear, and the last one is the longitudinal load distribution factor $K_{F\beta}$, which is the function of the helix angle β. However, these modified factors only approximately reflect the geometric properties, meshing characteristics, and mechanics properties of a CATT gear.

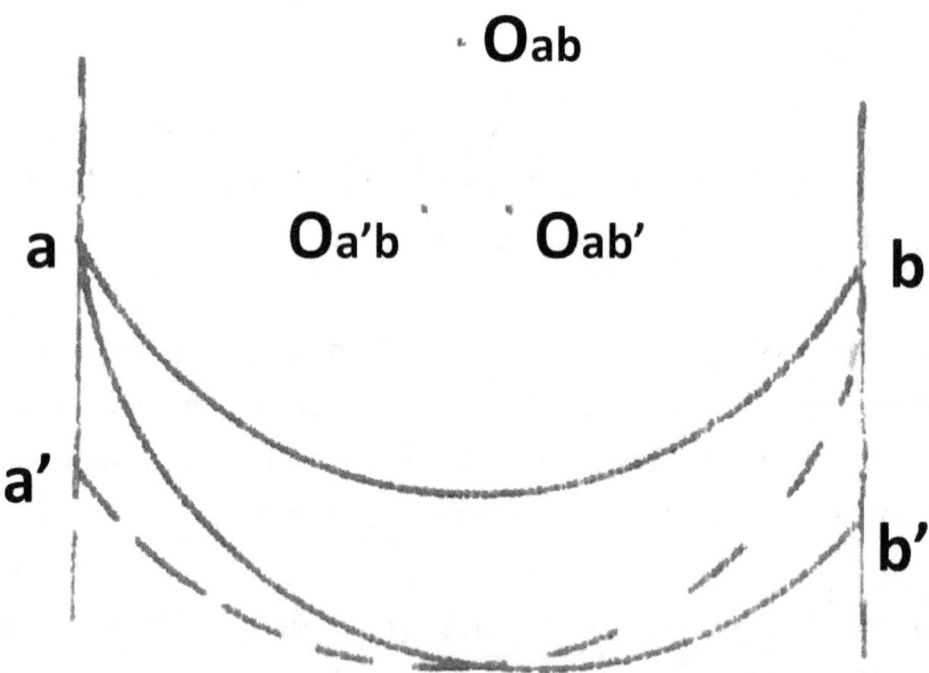

Figure 10.1 Tooth Traces for Three Cases: Desired Trace ab with Center Point O_{ab}, Actual Trace a'b with Center $O_{a'b}$ or Actual Trace ab' with Center Point $O_{ab'}$

10.2 EXPERIMENTAL ERROR ANALYSIS

The experimental errors are involved in the following aspects:

1) Manufacturing Accuracy Errors of a Pair of Experimental Gears: they come from the process of cutting an individual gear. Theoretically, a CATT gear is cut using one cutting tool with inside edge and outside edge for the convex tooth and the concave tooth, respectively (Peng, 1978). Actually, it uses two cutting

tools to cut the convex tooth and the concave tooth, respectively (Zhang, 1988). This raises the non-uniform contacts of two engaged teeth, such as the engagement happens on the two sides without the middle area contact or on the middle area without the two side contacts. Thus, it is necessary to use one cutting tool to cut one gear to reduce manufacturing errors.

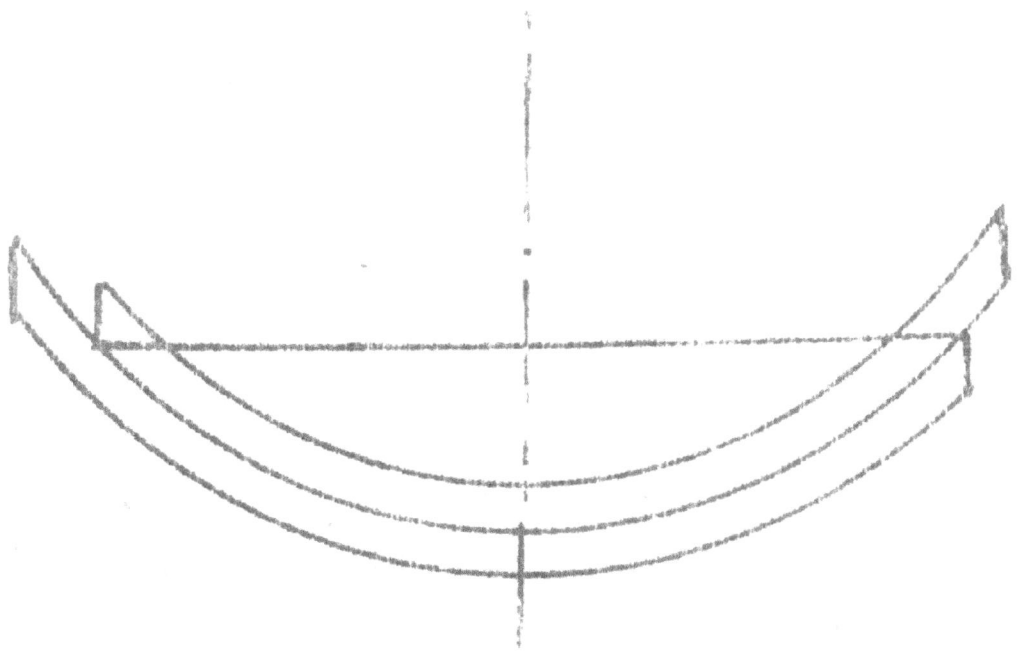

Figure 10.2 Centro-Symmetric Correction for Two Engaged Teeth

2) Workpiece Installation Errors: they come from the gear workpiece missing to align with the central axis as being installed in the cutting machine. The errors cause the center of the gear deviates from the center O_{ab} to $O_{a'b}$ or $O_{ab'}$ as indicated in Figure 10.1 (desired trace ab with center point O_{ab}, actual trace a'b with center $O_{a'b}$, or actual trace ab' with center point $O_{ab'}$). The problem is when two gears mesh, they are not able to be engaged in the style of centrosymmetric.

Figure 10.2 illustrates the action to reduce this error taken in this experiment. The method is to adjust the driving tooth to ensure it align to the tested tooth in the center. The disadvantage is the contact width has to be narrowed. However, this correction does not affect the measuring data.

3) Transverse Load Distribution Errors: the experiment sets that full load is applied on the top of a single tooth in static condition. In fact, the full load is shared by two teeth because CATT gear contact ratio is bigger than 1. Theoretically, this assumption is corrected by adding a contact ratio factor in Equation 8.2.

4) Strain Gauges Position Errors: theoretically, the critical section is determined according to the method of Hofer 30° tangential line; while experimentally, the strain gauges are approximately attached in the root fillet of the tested tooth.

5) Plate Deformation Errors: the plate in the loading device is a thin and long plate, as shown in Figure 9.2. Originally, it is a simple plate and mounted on the slotted block at the head. This kind of structure easily raises deflection. Thus, three supports are added to enhance its stiffness to ensure the meshing preciousness of the pair of teeth.

6) Driven Shaft Deflection Errors: the static torque is applied to the tested gear from a lever plus weights through a thin and long driven shaft, as shown in Figure 9.3. The deflation of the shaft affects the meshing accuracy of the pair of the gears and leads to the engagement errors of two experimental teeth.

7) Miscellaneous Errors: they depend on the accuracy of the loading device, shaft deflections, and accuracy of instruments, which are summarized as:
- The errors caused by the simplifications of the driving tooth.
- The manufacturing and fabrication errors of the loading device.
- The positioning errors of the driving device.
- Installation errors of all parts involved in the device.
- The indirect forms of measurement errors.

REFERENCES

1. Gere, J.M. and Timoshenko, S.P. 1997. Mechanics of Materials. PWS Publishing Company, Michigan, USA.
2. Peng, F.H. 1978. Circular Arc Tooth Trace Cylindrical Gear Investigation. Journal of Jilin University, No.1, pp.6-8.
3. Zhang, FeM. 1988. Cutting Circular Arc Tooth Trace Cylindrical Gear Using X53K Milling Machine. Journal of Engineering, No. 4, pp.23-24.

Appendix I: Determination of Tooth Width Factor

Tooth width factor φ is also named as width/diameter ratio (Li and Zhao, 1994), which is one of the design parameters of a CATT gear. Three geometric parameters related to the tooth width factor φ are the tooth width B, the reference circular radius R, and the central angle β_o. The relationship between φ with three parameters B, R, and β_o is expressed as mathematical equations in this Chapter. With the help of the general equivalent stress equation established in Chapter 5, the effect of the tooth width factor φ on the tooth stress of CATT gear is analyzed, and the range of φ=0.65-0.75 is suggested.

I.1 DEFINITION OF TOOTH WIDTH FACTOR

Figure 1 shows a schematic diagram of the critical section of the CATT gear tooth. The symbols used in this appendix are indicated there. A local Cartesian coordinate o(x, y) is attached to the critical section with the origin o at the centroid C_0. Horizontal axis x coincides with the horizontal neutral axis x_0x_0; and the vertical axis y coincides with the vertical neutral axis y_0y_0.

According to the assumption in Chapter 2, the radius of convex tooth trace R_1 equals to the one of concave tooth trace R_2 and equals to the reference-circular radius R, such as $R_1=R_2=R$. Tooth width factor φ is defined as tooth width B divided by two times of reference circular radius R.

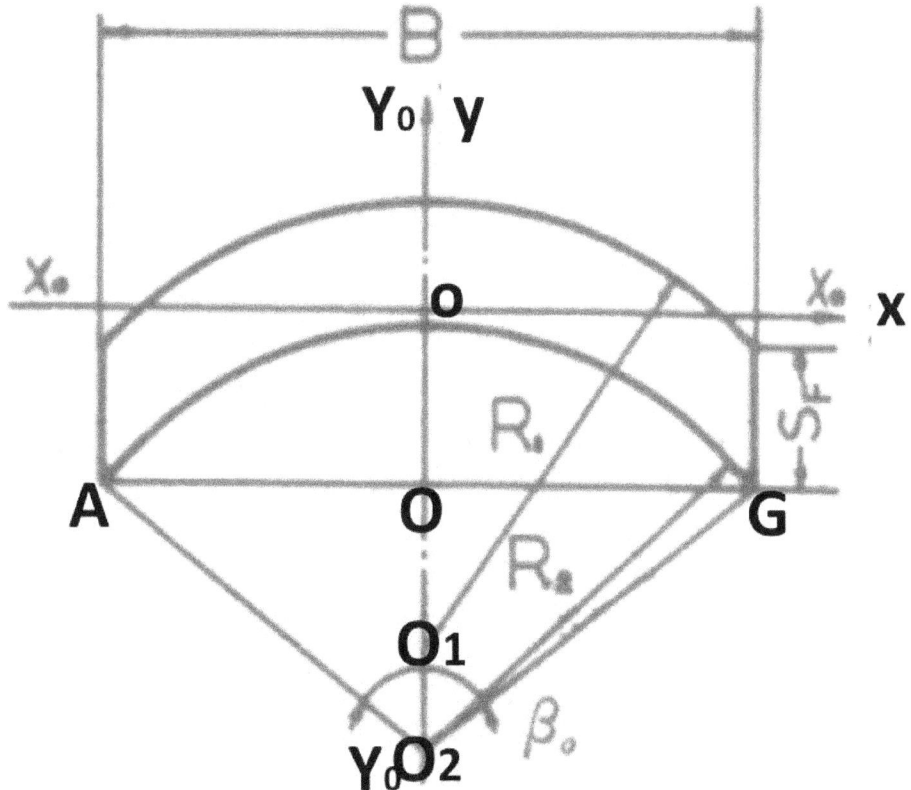

Figure 1 Schematic Diagram of Critical Section of CATT Gear Tooth

$$\varphi = \frac{B}{2R} \quad (1)$$

Also,

$$R = \frac{B}{2\varphi} \quad (2)$$

Referring to the right triangle OO_2G, it can be written as the function of the central angle β_o.

$$\varphi = \sin\frac{\beta_0}{2} \quad (3)$$

Equation 3 builds up the relationship between the tooth width factor φ and the central angle β_o. Sometimes, it is also expressed as Equation 4.

$$\beta_0 = 2\sin^{-1}\frac{B}{2R} = 2\sin^{-1}\varphi \qquad (4)$$

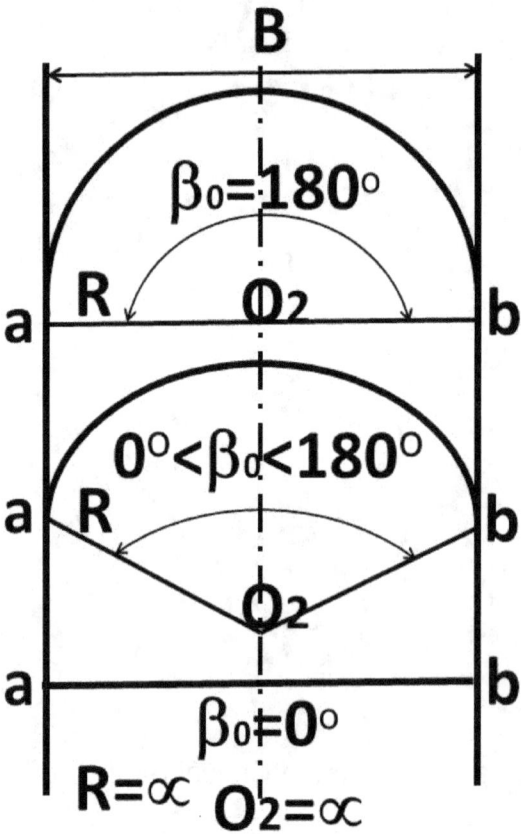

Figure 2 Variation of Reference Circular Radius R and Tooth Trace ab With Central Angle β_0 (or Tooth Width Factor φ) for a Given Tooth Width B

Theoretically, in Equation 3, it can find the tooth width factor φ can locate within the range of 0-1. Furthermore, in Equation 4, when the tooth width factor φ equals to 0, the central angle β_0 equals to 0°. It means this CATT gear becomes a spur gear. Then, when the tooth width factor φ equals to 1, the central angle β_0 equals to 180°. It means the tooth trace becomes semicircular arc and reaches the maximum value.

Figure 2 visualizes the variation of the reference-circular radius R and tooth trace ab with the central angle β_0 (or tooth width factor φ) for a given tooth width B. When the central angle β_0 increases from 0 to 180° (or φ=0-1), the reference-circular radius R decreases from the maximum ∝ to the minimum R=B/2; while the tooth trace ab increases from the minimum ab=B to the maximum ab=π*R. This visual result agrees with the above analysis result: when the tooth width factor φ equals to 0, CATT gear becomes a spur gear; while when the tooth width factor φ equals to 1, the tooth trace becomes semicircular arc and reaches the maximum value.

I.2 EFFECT OF TOOTH WIDTH FACTOR ON STRESS

Actually, in CATT gear design, it never selects the tooth width factor φ within the whole range from 0 to 1 without comparing the strength with other gears. It always intends to reduce tooth stress using CATT gear instead of spur gear or helical gear in industrial applications. So far, the range of φ=0.65-0.75 is suggested, considering the effect of tooth width factor φ on the tooth stress and manufacturing process. The manufacturing process is a big topic and has been discussed in some references (Arafa, 2005; Sonoda et al., 2014; Zhang et al., 2016). But, here, the topic is concentrated on the effect of the tooth width factor φ on the general equivalent stress σ_6.

General equivalent stress σ_6 on the critical section derived in Equation 5.12 in Chapter 5 is employed to analyze the influence of tooth width factor φ on the tooth stress. Equivalent stress σ_6 applied on the critical section is defined as the combination of the bending stress plus the compressive stress and the shear stress in terms of the strength theory of gear (Fan, 1979). Stress σ_6 reflects the general equivalent stress applied on the critical section. Here, it expressed as Equation 5.

$$\sigma_6 = P_t \sqrt{\left(\frac{h_F y}{I_{x0x0}} + \frac{\tan \alpha_n}{\beta_0 B S_F} \ln \frac{1+\varphi}{1-\varphi}\right)^2 + 2.5^2 \frac{1 + \frac{4}{\beta_0^2}\left(\ln \cos \frac{\beta_0}{2}\right)^2}{B^2 S_F^2}} \qquad (5)$$

where h_F is the distance between the critical section and the most unfavorable point, which can be calculated by Equation 3.1 in Chapter 3. I_{x0x0} is the moment of inertia of the critical section about the horizontal neutral axis x_0x_0, which can be obtained by Equation 4.15 in Chapter 4. S_F is the width of the critical section, which is given in Equation 3.2 in Chapter 3.

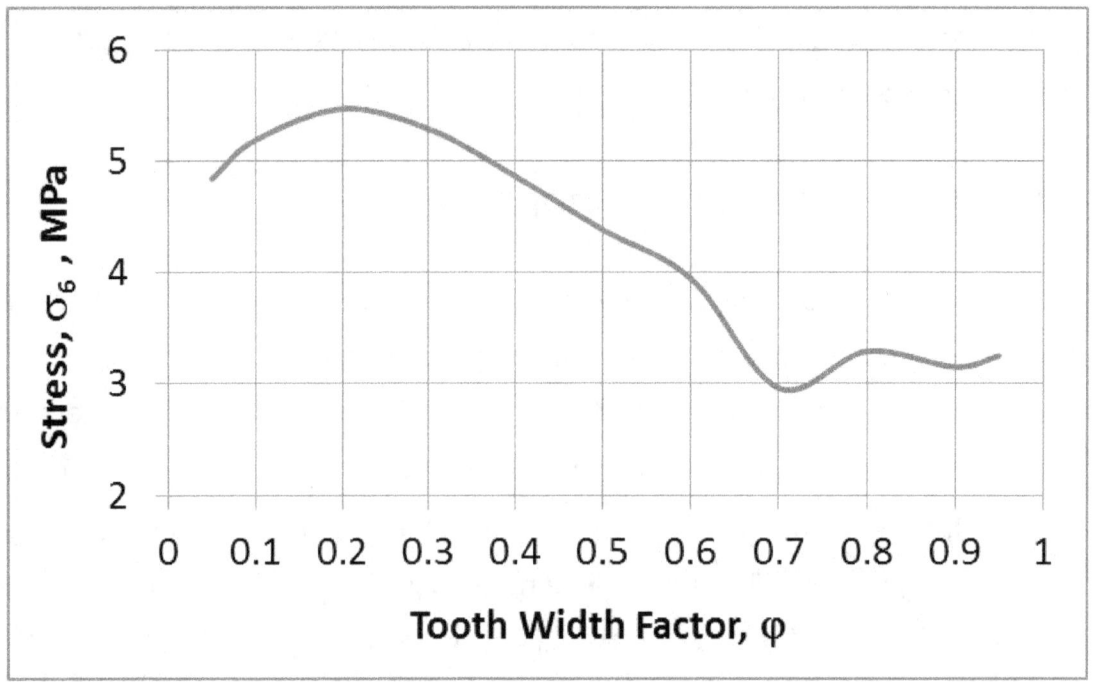

Figure 3 Stress σ_6 Variation with Tooth Width Factor φ at Root Fillets on Two Sides of Concave Tooth

Other items are given in Table **1**, where Z is the number of the calculation gear teeth, m is the module, α_n is the pressure angle at addendum circle, and B is the tooth width. It must emphasize that these four parameters assign in the middle transverse section. Remembering in Chapter 2, the tooth profile of a CATT gear is assumed to have a standard involute at any transverse section through the face width. In fact, as introduced in Figure 1.2, the transverse profile of a CATT gear tooth presents a standard involute only on the middle transverse section and approximately involutes on any other transverse profile.

Table 1 Basic CATT Gear Parameters at Middle Transverse Section

Number of Teeth (Z)	Module (m)	Pressure Angle (α_n)	Tooth Width (B)

19	5	20°	100mm

The loading condition is specified as: a tangential force of P_t=1000N is applied on the top of the concave tooth.

Figure 3 illustrates the variation of the general equivalent stress σ_6 with tooth width factor (φ=0.05-0.95) at root fillets on two sides (A and G) of the concave tooth. The reason to select these two points in this analysis is where the maximum stress σ_6 is predicted in Chapters 7-9.

For a given tooth width B, the stress σ_6 increases from 4.84 MPa to 5.47 MPa with the increase of tooth width factor φ from 0.05 to 0.2, conversely decreases from 4.47 MPa to 2.96 MPa with the increase of tooth width factor φ from 0.2 to 0.7, alternately, increases from 2.96 MPa to 3.29 MPa with the increase of tooth width factor φ from 0.7 to 0.8, and then fluctuates between 3.29 MPa and 3.25 MPa within the tooth width factor φ between 0.8 and 0.95. The maximum stress of 5.47 MPa appears in the tooth width factor φ equals to 0.2; while the minimum stress of 2.96 MPa appears in the tooth width factor φ equals to 0.7.

Generally speaking, the lower stress zones occur in range φ=0.65-0.1. But, it usually does not suggest choosing φ=0.75-0.1 as the design parameters. Just like the theoretical analysis in Section 1, the larger φ is, the longer the contact arc of a pair of teeth is. So far, the manufacturing accuracy degree is still a big obstacle to keep two meshed teeth coming into complete contact. This non-uniform contact makes the tangential force distribution present non-uniformly along the full tooth trace. It will cause the load intensity and enlarge the stress concentration at the root fillet.

Therefore, currently, it suggests the tooth width factor range is φ=0.65-0.75, where the lowest stress σ_6 zone locates in. It notes that within this range, the contact arc does not reach the longest one, but the stress σ_6 reaches the lowest value. In the manufacturing process, within this range, it can ensure two engaged teeth contact entirely and uniformly. All of these results show that choosing this range can meet the requirements for decreasing tooth stress towards increasing the strength in CATT gear design and development.

REFERENCES

1. Li, Y. and Zhao, X.Y. 1994. Influence of Tooth Width/Diameter Ratio on Tooth Stress of CATT Gear. Journal of North China Institute of Technology, Vol.15, No.4, pp.311-314.
2. Arafa, Hu., 2005. C-Gears: Geometry and Machining. ARCHIVE Proceedings of the Institution of Mechanical Engineers Part C Journal of Mechanical Engineering Science, 219(7), pp.709-726.
3. Sonoda, K., Takenouchi, K., and Hashimuras.. 2014. Design and Manufacture of New Circular-Arc Tooth-Trace Gears. The 3rd International Conference on Design Engineering and Science, ICDES.
4. Zhang, Q.L., Hou, R. and Tang, G.W.. 2016. Method of Processing and an Analysis of Meshing and Contact of Circular Arc Tooth Trace Cylindrical Gears. Transactions Of Famena XI-4, pp.11-14.
5. Fan, C.B. 1979. Gear Strength and Experiment. Mechanical Industry Publisher. Beijing, P.R. China.

AUTHOR'S NOTE

After publishing the first scientific research book written in English, I found a key to write an English language book in the mechanical engineering application. In fact, if I say it is a key rather than it is just self-confidence. When I was a master's degree candidate at the North University of China twenty-nine years ago, I never imagined that someday I was able to document my jobs in a book, and especially an English book in the USA. Anything can happen overnight instead of more than two decades.

Why Did I Write This Book?

Back to the time of 1987-1990, I undertook two roles: one was a graduate student, and another one was a teacher. As a student, I studied for earning my master's degree with three supervisors, Professor Xueyong Zhao, Associate Professor Lijun Wang, and Associate Professor Yihong Shi. As a teacher, I taught the mechanical design course with them in the same department. At the same time, they were not only my teachers but also my colleagues. They are always appreciated for giving me significant suggestions and advice with my project and teaching career. It is with much personal sadness that Professor Zhao and Professor Wang already passed away. God blesses them to be peaceful in heaven. It is so glad to know that Professor Shi lives in China. God blesses her to be healthy and have long lives.

Dr. Zhehui Liu is my husband and also my graduate college classmate. We both have been educated and worked in China, and then we traveled overseas to pursue our new lives. He had given me tremendous help with writing English language articles, which published in international conferences. Those practices built a foundation for me later to write many international journal articles so that I was full of confidence in writing books in English.

The topic of this book is about the bending strength of a special type of gear: circular-arc tooth-trace (CATT) cylindrical gear. The main sources come from my master's degree thesis. In the past two decades, I kept an eye on international publications and quite often searched the relevant topics, but fewer reports were found. It seemed the studies on this kind of gear were almost stopped due to hard manufacturing and other application problems. Gradually, this research area became pale from my brain.

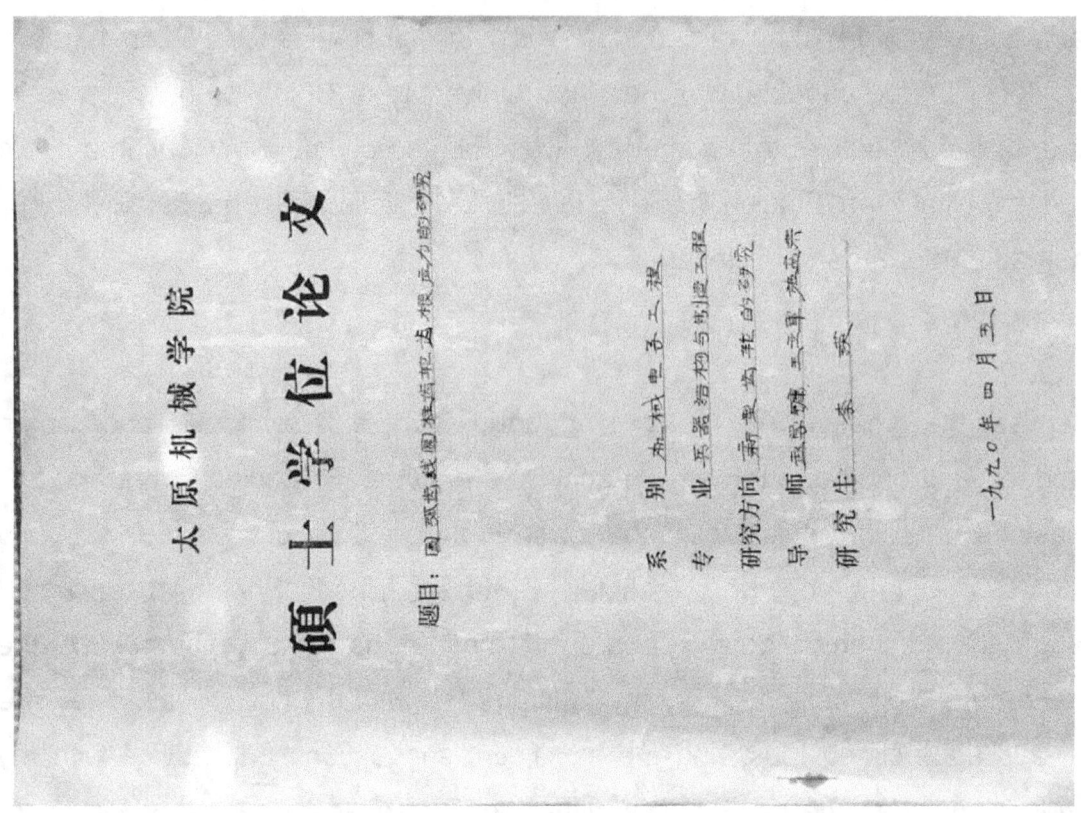

Figure 1 My Master Degree Thesis

The turning point came in 2017 as I visited my hometown and also my mother's college in China. In my mom's room, an old bookshelf drew me attention. To my surprise was that my master's degree thesis (see Figure 1) was still laid on her bookshelf after more than twenty-seven years. It was hard to believe she even kept my early publications. It was amazing that she knew how important those materials were for me. She had moved several times, and then those materials were never missed. She was deserved my deepest gratitude again. I was so proud of having such a knowledgeable mother and was touched by her concern and attention. This brushed feeling trigged me to reread them. I found that some of our early jobs still took a significant role in the new type of gear research & development field. This fact inspired me to re-pick up the topics. My self-confidence promoted me to translate the thesis into an English language book for sharing ideas worldwide. Just because of this trip, I would be able to bring the thesis and all publications to the USA as the primary materials for writing this book.

How Did I Write This Book?

Nothing is easy, but nothing is impossible. I started at the chapter of mechanics modeling of the tooth. Translation from Chinese into English was a big challenge because I was not familiar with the gear terminology in English. Living overseas, I have learned a large amount of English technical languages on the mining machinery in past decades. Unfortunately, I never touched any technical terminology related to the gear area. Even though I had enough materials to fill in my book, my brain didn't have enough English words to express them. It was absolutely not a good idea to translate words one by one. Google translator was helpful but not perfect because some of the terminologies were not translated correctly. My steps became slower and had to search for the relevant articles for references. The problem just liked I mentioned before, and there wasn't enough this kind of publication written using the native English language. Some publications were written by schoolers who had English as a second language. The technical methodologies were right, but there were many grammar problems.

At that moment, my three international conference articles (see Figure 2) published twenty years ago did a great help to me. They were written by cutting and translating from my master's degree thesis. My husband did most translating jobs for all three. His writing skill was better than mine because, by that time, he had already published more than ten articles in international journals. Taking this space, I would like to offer him my sincere appreciation for his support and motivation. Referring to those articles, I got the clue for my book. The terminologies in three articles were enough to support me in writing fluently in English. I didn't copy all the things from them rather than I had added many more new thoughts in the book.

Furthermore, I reorganized my publications, reports, test data, and thesis. Some of them had been done at the university when I worked as a graduate student. Some of them had been published in the Chinese language. Facing these publications and documents, my mind was running. I suddenly realized my career in the CATT gear field, which has stopped for more than twenty years, could be lasted again in the future if I didn't give up.

My motivation to write this book was inspired, and I started to put extreme enthusiasm to work on this book. This work is my second time writing a scientific research book using the English language. It needs knowledge, experience, writing skills, patience, encouragement, and strength. It seemed no more difficult to do this project than to do the first book since I already knew how to organize and arrange a book. The more I write, the more I feel excited. I could not be able to stop my writing and even weekend days. Until one day, I felt my eyes were tearing and painful; I had had to stop for several weeks and try to take a rest, empty mind, and calm down.

Restarting to work on this book, I reformed my way. For example, I divided the working time into several short segments. Every time, I concentrated on one sub-topic and controlled time within one hour and then forced me to pause for doing the eye exercise. Just following this kind of arrangement, I finished section by section and chapter by chapter.

The job went to the experiment part. All the experimental devices and instruments were designed and manufactured by me twenty-eight years ago. I doubted if the method was new enough to share with the reader. I searched some experimental techniques used to measure other kinds of gears and found the fundamental principles were the same. Actually, the sharing idea is my purpose in this book. The method may not be perfect, but sometimes it doesn't need to be perfect. I realized that if I constantly worried about if my book could be perfect, I would never get it done. I just want all readers can get some useful information from my job.

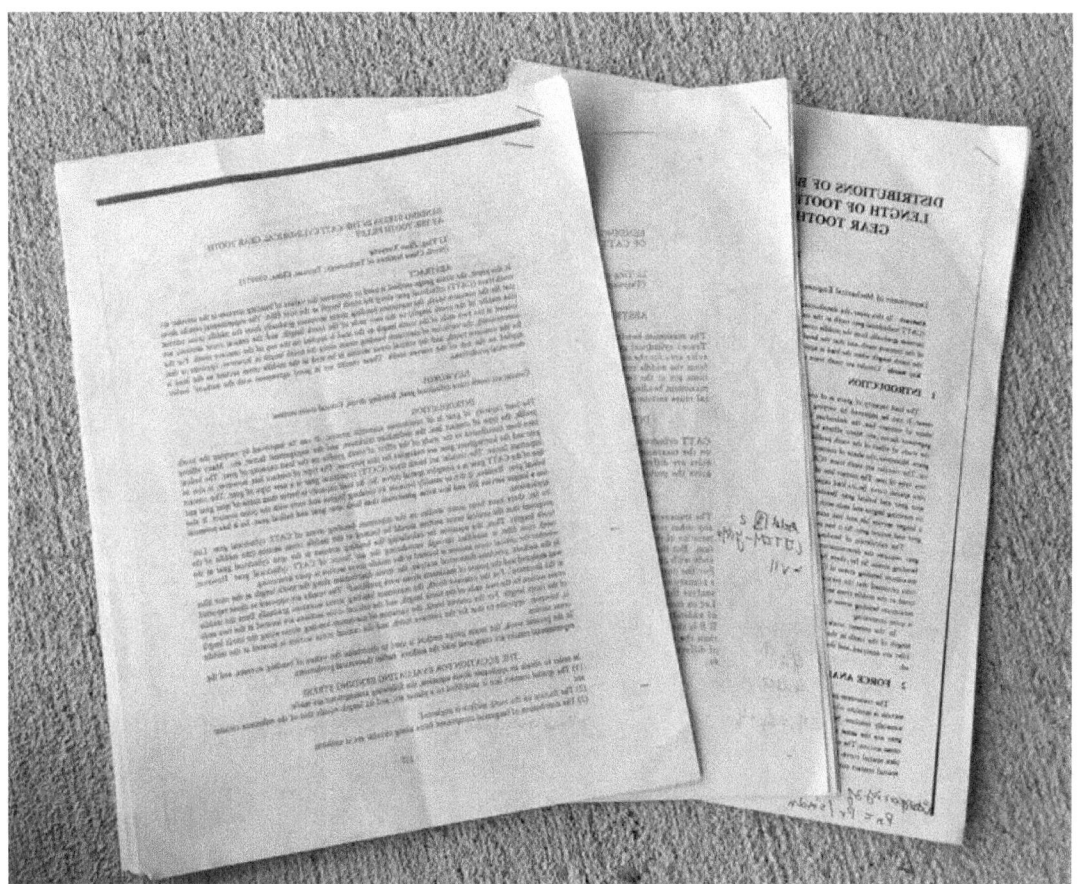

Figure 2 Three International Conference Articles

In 2018, my efforts brought this book to completion. It took around ten months to achieve this project, while preparation may last ten years or even more decades. I can say that the book was started with my three years' graduate study from accumulating materials through setting up experiments to documenting the thesis. I want to say that it came from my constant research during twelve years' faculty experience. I have to say that it also came from my overseas practices in the academic and industrial fields. Now, the book is drafted in a manuscript and published. This long journey eventually comes to an end as a result of a book, which condensates the efforts of all contributors.

About Author

Dr. Ying Li lives in the USA with her family. She has focused on mining machinery research since 1997. She has been a Principal Engineer at Bucyrus International Inc., USA; a Post-doctor Research Fellow at the University of Missouri-Rolls, USA; a Post-doctor Research Fellow at the University of Alberta, Canada; a PhD Candidate at the University of Science and Technology Beijing, China and a faculty at the North University of China, China. Her research interests include mining equipment dynamics modeling, virtual prototype simulation and structural strength analysis. She has published more than 70 publications on the mechanical science and engineering fields.

She has been a teacher, researcher and engineer. She dreamed of someday writing a book. Now, this dream is multiplied to 9 books, which include seven personal memoirs books [1-7], one healthcare book [8] and one scientific research book [9].

Her personal memoirs books [1-7] tell a bunch of stories about her personal experiences in the life journey to inspire people to be strong and have faith when facing big challenges. Her books have helped many people going through tough times.

Her healthcare book [8] shares the menopause experiences she had seen, heard and read. She wishes to encourage people who are troubled by menopause. Her book has helped them learn menopause symptoms and overcome their impact on physiology and spirit.

Her scientific research book [9] introduces the virtual prototype modeling and dynamics simulation of cable shovel for advanced engineering analysis.

The book condenses the research results she has accumulated when she worked on the heavy machinery area. She hopes to contribute her knowledge to academia and industry.

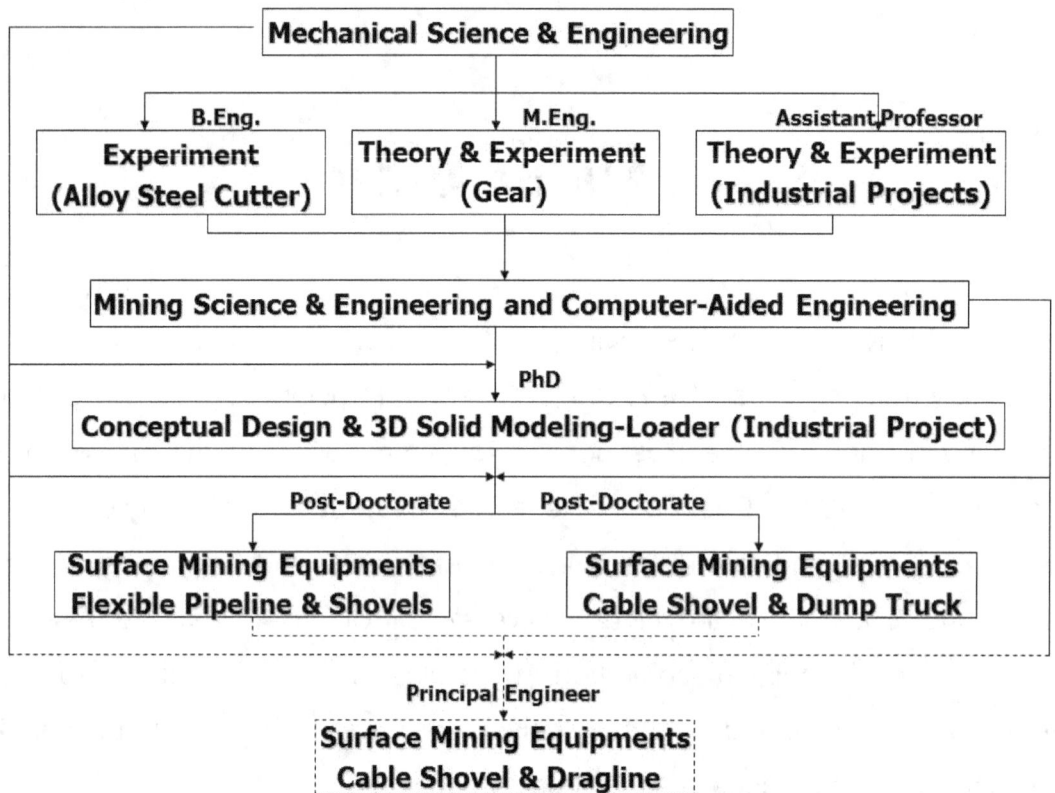

Ying Li Career Experience

BOOKS BY YING LI

1. Li Y. Life Is Unpredictable and Nobody Life Is Perfect. CreateSpace Independent Publishing Platform, ISBN-13: 9781979531894, ISBN-10: 1979531897, Nov., 2017.

2. Li Y. Nothing is Promised, Thinking Positive in the Tough Time CreateSpace Independent Publishing Platform, ISBN-13: 9781539328667, ISBN-10: 153932866X, September 23, 2016.

3. Li Y. Dance in the Rain. CreateSpace Independent Publishing Platform, ISBN-13: 9781534669352, ISBN-10: 1534669353, June 13, 2016.

4. Li Y. Random Thoughts for 2016 Album. CreateSpace Independent Publishing Platform, ISBN-13: 9781532958748, ISBN-10: 1532958749, April 30, 2016.

5. Li Y. Random Thoughts for 2015 Album. CreateSpace Independent Publishing Platform, ISBN-13: 9781530145775, ISBN-10: 1530145775, February 20, 2016.

6. Li Y. Life Is Long Drive. CreateSpace Independent Publishing Platform, ISBN-10: 150317932X, ISBN-13: 978-1503179325, January 27, 2014.

7. Li Y. Gone with the Waves-Letters Sent to My Family. CreateSpace Independent Publishing Platform, ISBN-10: 1495303527, ISBN-13: 978-1495303524, January 27, 2015.

8. Li Y. Experiencing Menopause: Be Healthy, Be Happy, Be Strong and Be Self-motivated (Chinese Edition). CreateSpace Independent Publishing Platform, ISBN-13: 97819795803902. ISBN-10: 1979803906, Aug 26, 2017.

9. Li Y., Samuel Frimpong and Yi Zheng. Virtual Prototype Modeling and Dynamics Simulation of Cable Shovel for Advance Engineering Analysis. CreateSpace Independent Publishing Platform, ISBN/EAN13:1545459495 / 978154545949, Apr. 20, 2017.

10. Bending Strength of Circular-Arc-Tooth-Trace Cylindrical Gear: Theoretical Modelling and Experimental Validation. Independent Publishing Platform, ISBN-13: 978-1729625132, ISBN-10: 1729625134, Nov.1, 2018.

www.ingramcontent.com/pod-product-compliance
Lightning Source LLC
Chambersburg PA
CBHW062329220526
45469CB00008B/2641